Discovering
Algebra
An Investigative Approach

Discovering Algebra with TI-Navigator™

DISCOVERING

MATHEMATICS™

Key Curriculum Press
Innovators in Mathematics Education

Teacher's Materials Project Editor:	Elizabeth DeCarli
Editor:	Josephine Noah
Project Administrator:	Aaron Madrigal
Writers:	Judy Hicks, Steven P. Isaak, Lauren L. Jensen
Accuracy Checker:	Abigail R. Hernandez
Project Manager:	Rose Rummel-Eury, Interactive Composition Corporation
Editorial Production Supervisor:	Christine Osborne
Production Supervisor:	Ann Rothenbuhler
Production Director:	McKinley Williams
Text Designer:	Jenny Somerville
Composition, Technical Art, Prepress:	Interactive Composition Corporation
Cover Designers:	Jensen Barnes, Jill Kongabel, Marilyn Perry
Printer:	Data Reproductions
Textbook Product Manager:	James Ryan
Executive Editor:	Casey FitzSimons
Publisher:	Steven Rasmussen

Cover Photo Credits: Background image: Pat O'Hara/DRK Photo. Boat image: Marc Epstein/DRK Photo. All other images: Ken Karp Photography.

Limited Reproduction Permission

***Discovering Algebra with TI-Navigator* CD-ROM**

Key Curriculum Press guarantees that the CD-ROM that accompanies this book is free of defects in materials and workmanship. A defective CD-ROM will be replaced free of charge if returned within 90 days of the purchase date.

Key Curriculum Press
1150 65th Street
Emeryville, CA 94608
510-595-7000
editorial@keypress.com
www.keypress.com

Printed in the United States of America

10 9 8 7 6 5 4 3   11 10 09 08

ISBN 978-1-55953-853-4

Contents

Activity Numbers here refer to the corresponding lesson in *Discovering Algebra*. Not every lesson in the student book is represented here.

Chapter 6

Chapter 7

Chapter 8

Chapter 9

Chapter 11

Discovering Algebra with TI-Navigator™
© 2007 Key Curriculum Press

Introduction

The activities in this book are a resource to help enrich your *Discovering Algebra* classroom with the use of TI-Navigator. Many of the activities walk you through how to run an investigation from the student text with the enhancement of TI-Navigator. Others use TI-Navigator's Activity Center to interactively explore an activity's topics. Still others help you assess students with the help of LearningCheck™ files. All activities are written as Teacher Notes that guide you step by step in how to conduct your class using TI-Navigator. Occasionally a student worksheet is included as well.

This book starts with a few Tip Sheets that describe how to use common features of TI-Navigator. The Tip Sheets on Logging In and LearningCheck Tips can be passed out to students. The Tip Sheet on Quick Polls and Screen Captures is for teacher use.

Additionally, LearningCheck files are provided to help you assess students throughout the year.

What's on the CD

The CD that accompanies this book contains all the TI-Navigator activity files, list and program files, and other electronic files you need to run these activities. Note that the activities are written assuming the use of a TI-83 Plus or TI-84 Plus, but list and program files are also provided for the TI-73. Also provided are LearningCheck files for use with various lessons throughout the year. Additionally, a number of Software Tours created by Texas Instruments, Inc., are included, which provide details on how to use particular features of TI-Navigator. These Software Tours are listed below. If you need further assistance with setting up or using TI-Navigator, see the documentation that came with your TI-Navigator system.

TI-Navigator Software Tours (PDFs)

Collecting Files

Contributing Equations in Activity Center

Contributing Lists in Activity Center

Contributing Points in Activity Center

Creating Class and Adding Students

Deleting Files

Exporting Student Results from Class Analysis

Importing Students

Installing TI-Navigator Calculator Apps

Loading Student Responses into Class Analysis

Polling from Teacher Calculator

Receiving Files from Student Calculators

Tip Sheet

Logging In

To log in on your calculator, you'll run the application NavNet. To do this, follow these steps:

1. Press APPS.

2. Scroll down (or press ALPHA-[N]) to the application NavNet, and press ENTER. Press any key to continue.

3. Enter the Username and Password given to you by your teacher, then press OK (Y=).

4. You are now logged in. You have four options: 1: ACTIVITY CENTER, 2: NETWORK APPS, 3: TRANSFERS, and 4: EXIT APP. Your teacher will tell you which to choose. Press 1, 2, 3, or 4, or use the arrow buttons to scroll to the choice you want, and press ENTER.

Tip Sheet

LearningCheck Tips

These tips will help you navigate through a LearningCheck document on your calculator.

- Select PIC or TXT to move between the picture and text for a particular question.

- Select Q or ANS to move between the question and answer for a particular question.

- Always press ENTER to select your answer. If you move to the answer but do not press ENTER, your answer will not be recorded.

- For fill-in-the-blank or free-response questions, you'll default to typing capital letters. To switch to lowercase letters, press ALPHA once. To switch to numbers, press ALPHA again.

- For pull-down menus, press any key to see the answer choices.

- Select NEXT to move to the next question.

- You can always select MENU to see a list of options. You can go back to the previous item or see a list of items and choose which one you want. You can redo problems if you like. (In the MENU screen, answered questions have a small square next to them.)

Discovering Algebra with TI-Navigator™
© 2007 Key Curriculum Press

Tip Sheet

Quick Polls and Screen Captures

To conduct a Quick Poll, follow these steps:

1. Be sure that your students are logged in to NavNet.

2. On the TI-Navigator home screen or in the Activity Center, click the *Quick Poll* icon. The "Quick Poll" window will open.

3. Choose the answer choices you prefer. Your choices are: Agree Disagree 5, Agree Disagree 3, Agree Disagree 2, Yes No, True False, Right Wrong, Aways Sometimes Never, Multiple Choice A Thru E, Multiple Choice A Thru D, Multiple Choice A Thru C, Multiple Choice A Thru B, and Open Response. The first three options give you a scale of agree to disagree with five, three, or two choices.

4. In the upper left corner, check "Resubmit" if you want students to be able to change their answers. If you like, you can type the poll question or any other text into the "Poll Prompt" blank.

5. Click **Start Poll.**

6. Students will see the answer options on their calculators. They use the arrow buttons to scroll through the options. When their preferred answer is marked, they press SEND ([Y=]). You'll see student answers appear on the screen as they are sent in.

7. You can click **Pause Poll** or **Resume Poll** at any time. Click **Stop Poll** when finished.

8. You can click **Send Results** to send a bar chart of student responses to all students' calculators.

9. Close the "Quick Poll" window.

To take Screen Captures, follow these steps:

1. Be sure that your students are logged in to NavNet.

2. On the TI-Navigator home screen, click the *Screen Capture* icon. Click the *Class* icon if you wish to take Screen Captures of all students' calculators, or click *Students* and select only the students you want. (Hold the Ctrl key to select more than one student.) Click **OK.** The "Screen Capture" window will open, showing the screens of all students you have selected.

3. Check "Show Student Names" to show students' usernames. Click **Refresh screens** to refresh screens.

4. Close the "Screen Capture" window.

Activity 1.1 Teacher Notes

In this activity, students follow steps similar to those in the Picturing Pulse Rates investigation. First, Quick Polls will be introduced and used to create bar charts. Then, TI-Navigator will be used further to assist in picturing pulse rates and completing the investigation in the text.

Activity Time: 40–50 minutes

PREREQUISITES AND MATERIALS

You will need the file **1-1 Picturing Pulse Rates.act** and the materials listed in the Teacher's Edition for the Picturing Pulse Rates investigation.

SETTING UP THE ACTIVITY

On the TI-Navigator teacher computer home screen, click the *Activity Center* icon. Choose **File | Load | Load Activity Settings** and load the activity settings file **1-1 Picturing Pulse Rates.act.**

Click the **Graph** tab within the Activity Center.

RUNNING THE ACTIVITY

Prepare your students for the activity by explaining that they will first be answering polling questions using their calculators, and then discuss the class's responses. Then students will complete the Picturing Pulse Rates investigation and share their data using TI-Navigator.

1. On the TI-Navigator home screen, click the **Begin Class** button. Ask students to log in on their calculators. To do this, students press [APPS], scroll down (or press [ALPHA]-[N]) to the application NavNet, press [ENTER], and then enter their Username and Password and press OK ([Y=]). Make sure all students are logged in.

2. On the TI-Navigator home screen, click the *Quick Poll* icon. The "Quick Poll" window will open.

There are several Quick Poll answering options, which can be viewed in the pull-down menu at the top of the "Quick Poll" window. Among the options are yes/no; true/false; multiple choice with 3, 4, or 5 options; agree/disagree with a scale of 1–2, 1–3, or 1–5; and open response. When you ask a Quick Poll question, you can type the question into the "Poll Prompt" blank at the top of the "Quick Poll" window, you can announce the question verbally, or you might write the question and answer options on the board or on a transparency.

3. Select the polling option "Yes No." Ask the following question: Do you have a sibling? (You may need to explain that a sibling is a brother or sister.) Click **Start Poll.** Students will arrow to YES or NO and press SEND ([Y=]). TI-Navigator will keep track of students' answers in a bar chart. (Once students have sent their answers, they cannot change their answers, unless you check the "Resubmit" box before starting the poll.)

4. When all students have entered their responses, click **Stop Poll.**

Q1 Allow students to interpret the results shown on the screen by asking the class these questions:

- How many students have a sibling?

- What is the difference between the number of classmates that have siblings and the number that do not?

5. Try another Quick Poll. Select the polling option "Multiple Choice A through E." Write this question and its answer options on the board.

    Select your favorite type of music from the following list:

    A.   Rock

    B.   Country

    C.   Rap

    D.   Pop

    E.   Other

Click **Start Poll.** Students should again arrow down to the desired answer and press SEND ([Y=]), and answers will again be displayed in a bar chart. Click **Stop Poll** when finished.

Q2 To encourage interpretation of the data, you might ask questions such as these: What type of music is most popular in this class? What type of music is least popular in this class? How many students prefer either rock or pop music? How many students prefer either rap or country? The number of students who listen to rap is equal to the sum of what two other groups of music?

You might conduct a few more Quick Polls on topics of interest to your students. Try at least one open response poll.

You can send the results of a Quick Poll to students. To do this, after you have clicked **Stop Poll,** click the **Send Results** button. Students press QUIT ([GRAPH]) to exit this display. Close the "Quick Poll" window.

Now students will work through the Picturing Pulse Rates investigation, and they'll create a dynamic dot plot using TI-Navigator's Activity Center.

6. Ask students to collect pulse rate data as described in the Procedure Note of the investigation. Instruct students to select 1: ACTIVITY CENTER. Students will see the message "WAITING FOR TEACHER." In the Activity Center, click the **Start Activity** button.

Now students will use the Activity Center to create a dot plot.

7. Select **View | Individualize Student Cursors.** (If there is already a check next to this option, you don't need to select it again.) This allows students to more easily identify which cursor is theirs.

In this activity's settings your students have a Step Size of 1. That is, their cursors move one unit every time they press an arrow key.

8. One at a time, have students state their pulse rate, and use their calculator's arrows to move their cursor to the appropriate place on the number line. The x-value will be their pulse rate and the y-value can be anything. Then press MARK ($\boxed{Y=}$). A point appears on the calculator's screen. At the same time, the point appears in the Activity Center on the teacher's computer. All students should record every student's pulse rate on their paper. (You should write them on the board also.) If a student has a pulse rate that has already been recorded by at least one other student, ask about an appropriate way of handling this. It's likely that students will think of "stacking" dots. Pressing PLOT ($\boxed{ZOOM}$) will plot the entire class's points on students' calculators.

9. Now continue with Steps 2–7 of the Picturing Pulse Rates investigation.

When students have completed the investigation, you can use Quick Polls to check understanding. You can click the *Quick Poll* icon in the Activity Center, rather than returning to the TI-Navigator home screen.

Q3 Do a Quick Poll set to "Open Response" and ask, "What is the minimum (lowest) value in the pulse rate data?"

Q4 Do a Quick Poll set to "Open Response" and ask, "What is the maximum value of the data set?"

Q5 Do a Quick Poll set to "Open Response" and ask, "What is the range of the data?"

In this activity, students follow steps similar to those in the Hand Spans investigation. TI-Navigator allows students to share their data easily. In this activity you will use TI-Navigator to aggregate student data, to take Screen Captures to check student progress and understanding, and to display students' calculator histograms.

Activity Time: 25–40 minutes

PREREQUISITES AND MATERIALS

You will need the Navigator activity file **1-4 Hand Spans.act.**

SETTING UP THE ACTIVITY

On the TI-Navigator teacher computer home screen, click the *Activity Center* icon. Choose **File | Load | Load Activity Settings** and load the activity settings file **1-4 Hand Spans.act.**

Click the **List** tab within the Activity Center.

RUNNING THE ACTIVITY

1. On the TI-Navigator home screen, click the **Begin Class** button. Ask students to log in on their calculators and go to the Activity Center. To do this, students press APPS, scroll down (or press ALPHA-[N]) to the application NavNet, press ENTER, and then enter their Username and Password and press OK ([Y=]). Then, students select 1: ACTIVITY CENTER. Students will see the message "WAITING FOR TEACHER." Make sure all students are logged in. Then return to the Activity Center and click the **Start Activity** button. Students will receive an empty list.

2. Instruct students to measure their hand span as described in Step 1 of the Hand Spans investigation, enter it into the empty list L1 on their calculators, and send their data. To do this, students type in their data value, press ENTER, and press SEND ([Y=]). As students send data, the Activity Center's list will grow. Students have the option of re-entering a piece of data to ensure it is correct.

3. Click **Pause Activity** after you think all students have entered their data, and ask if everyone has contributed their measurement. If not, click **Resume Activity** to allow any remaining students to send data. Then click **Stop Activity.**

4. Click **Configure,** change to "Students start with: Existing activity lists," and click **OK.** Click **Start Activity** again. Students will now receive an aggregated data list in L1, which will include all the class data. Click **Stop Activity.**

5. Instruct students to exit NavNet. To do this, they press [2ND] [QUIT], and select 4: EXIT APP. The class data can now be found in list L1 on each student's calculator. (To see L1, students press [STAT] and select 1: Edit... .)

6. Have students work through Steps 2–6 of the Hand Spans investigation, using the class data in L1.

Q1 Ask students how they might select a good bin width for their histogram.

Calculator Note 1E describes how to create histograms on the calculator.

7. Have students explore making histograms of various bin widths on their calculators. As they experiment, check progress by taking Screen Captures. (Do not project your computer's display while you do this.) To do this, on the TI-Navigator home screen, click the *Screen Capture* icon. Click the *Class* icon, and click **OK.** After some time, have students select their best histogram and display it on their calculator screen. Take a Screen Capture of all student calculators (you can click the **Refresh screens** button if the Screen Capture window is already open), project the Screen Captures for student viewing, and have various groups present their histograms and discuss why they selected their bin widths.

8. Have students continue working on Steps 8–9 of the investigation.

In this activity, TI-Navigator will be used as a formative assessment tool. Formative assessment is interactive and should support growth over time. TI-Navigator is ideal for formative assessment because you can use it to provide immediate feedback to reinforce learning objectives. Formative assessment activities need not count toward a grade—this particular LearningCheck document is meant to help you gather information about students' knowledge. This activity can be used as a follow-up to the Guesstimating investigation. TI-Navigator will be used to send LearningCheck files to students' calculators, and the activity concludes with an analysis of students' responses.

Activity Time: 10–15 minutes. If you wish to also review answers with the class using a slide show, this activity might take as much as 30 minutes.

PREREQUISITES AND MATERIALS

You will need the LearningCheck file **1-7 Estimating.edc.**

SETTING UP THE ACTIVITY

For information on how to write your own LearningCheck files, see the TI-Navigator Software Tour "Using TI LearningCheck Creator and Class Analysis."

From the TI-Navigator teacher computer home screen, click **Begin Class** and click the *Send to Class* icon. Select the file **1-7 Estimating.edc** and click **Next.** Click the *Class* icon, check "Force send to students now," and click **Finish.**

Prepare your students for the activity by explaining that they will be taking an assessment on their calculators and then you will be retrieving their answers.

RUNNING THE ACTIVITY

1. Ask students to log in on their calculators. To do this, students press APPS, scroll down (or press ALPHA-[N]) to the application NavNet, press ENTER, and then enter their Username and Password and press OK (Y=). They will immediately see files being transferred to their calculators. When the calculator says "TRANSFERS COMPLETE," students should press BACK (ZOOM). Now instruct students to select 2: NETWORK APPS.

2. Tell students to select LearnChk by pressing ENTER. Students will then see an assignment list. Tell students to arrow down to estimating and press ENTER.

3. Students should work through the assessment on their calculators. If this is the first LearningCheck assessment they have done, they will need some time to

experiment and figure out how to navigate through the file and select answers. Write these hints on the board, or distribute the Tip Sheet on page viii:

- Select PIC or TXT to move between the picture and text for a particular question.

- Select Q or ANS to move between the question and answer for a particular question.

- Always press ENTER to select your answer. If you move to the answer but do not press ENTER, your answer will not be recorded.

- For fill-in-the-blank or free-response questions, you'll default to typing capital letters. To switch to lower case letters, press ALPHA once. To switch to numbers, press ALPHA again.

- For pull-down menus, press any key to see the answer choices.

- Select NEXT to move to the next question.

- You can always select MENU to see a list of options. You can go back to the previous item or see a list of items and choose which one you want. You can redo problems if you like. (In the MENU screen, answered questions have a small square next to them.)

For help with Screen Captures, see the Tip Sheet.

4. As students work through the assessment, you can click the *Screen Capture* icon on the TI-Navigator home screen to view students' calculator screens and check that students are on task and making progress.

Now you'll retrieve the class data.

5. To retrieve class data, click the *Class Analysis* icon on the TI-Navigator home screen. Click the *Collect Answer Files From Classroom Devices* icon to retrieve the data from student calculators. A "Collect Answer Files from Class" dialog box opens. Check "Delete Answer File from Device after Collect" and "Delete Assignment File from Device after Collect." Then click **Start Transfer.** (If some students did not take the quiz, you'll get an "External Request" message. Click **OK** and then, when all student files have been collected, click **Stop** on the left side of the screen, where it says "External Request.")

For more information on how to use Class Analysis, see the TI-Navigator Software Tour "Using TI LearningCheck Creator and Class Analysis."

Answer data is collected from the student calculators and displayed in a spreadsheet. Each student's data is stored as a separate file (called a user file) with the file extension ".usf." The Class Analysis program displays all of these individual files as one spreadsheet. The data will not be lost unless the files are deleted. You can print, save, or view the data in a slide show.

You'll now display results in a slide show and discuss the results with your class.

6. In the Class Analysis window, click the *Class Results Slide Show* icon. The slide show contains each question followed by a bar chart showing the number of students who entered each answer option. The buttons at the top of the screen allow you to stop the slide show, return to the beginning, move back one slide, move forward one slide, or move to the end of the slide show.

7. Move through the slide show with students, and discuss any interesting results. Be sure to point out common mistakes and address how to avoid them.

In this activity, students follow steps similar to those in the Converting Centimeters to Inches investigation. Students gather measurements of various objects around the room in both centimeters and inches. They then use this data to find a ratio to convert inches to centimeters and centimeters to inches.

TI-Navigator allows students to share their data easily and compile class data. The activity also uses Screen Captures and Quick Polls to help you evaluate student understanding.

Activity Time: 20–30 minutes

PREREQUISITES AND MATERIALS

Use this activity only if students are familiar with how to enter data into lists on their graphing calculators.

You will need the TI-Navigator activity file **2-3 Convert Cm to In.act.** Each group will need a yardstick or tape measure with inches marked, and a meterstick or tape measure with centimeters marked.

SETTING UP THE ACTIVITY

From the TI-Navigator teacher computer home screen, click the *Activity Center* icon. Choose **File | Load | Load Activity Settings** and load the activity settings file **2-3 Convert Cm to In.act.**

Click the **List** tab within the Activity Center.

RUNNING THE ACTIVITY

For help logging in, see the Tip Sheet.

1. Click the **Start Activity** button. Ask students to log in on their calculators and go to the Activity Center. They will see two empty lists.

2. Tell students to measure objects in the room in both inches and centimeters, as described in Step 1 of the Converting Centimeters to Inches investigation. Have them measure as many different items as possible within five minutes. Instruct them to enter the measurements in inches into calculator list L1 and the measurements in centimeters into list L2 and press SEND ([Y=]) to send the data.

3. Once all students have sent their data, click **Stop Activity.**

4. Now you'll combine all the students' data and send it back to them in two aggregated lists. To do this, click the **Configure** button, select "Existing activity lists," and click **OK.**

5. Click **Start Activity** again, and students will receive the aggregated lists on their calculators in L1 and L2. Click **Stop Activity.**

6. Instruct students to exit the Activity Center and continue with Step 2 of the Converting Centimeters to Inches investigation, using the class data that is in their calculator lists. You may need to discuss what to do with any strange data or outlying data points.

For help with Screen Captures, see the Tip Sheet.

7. As students work on Step 2, do Screen Captures to check for student understanding on how to use list operations to create list L3.

For help with Quick Polls, see the Tip Sheet.

8. For Step 4, do a Quick Poll set to "Open Response" and have students enter their ratios. TI-Navigator will automatically convert ratios to decimals. Click **Stop Poll.** To see the ratios entered by students, click the **Poll Details** tab.

Q1 Ask students what accounts for any variation in this ratio, and how many decimal places of accuracy are appropriate.

9. Take Screen Captures to check for understanding as students work through Step 5.

10. For Step 6, do two Quick Polls set to "Open Response" for parts a and b.

EXPLORE MORE

Have students measure a few items in either inches or centimeters (but not both), and then use their ratios to convert to the other measurement.

Activity 2.4

In this activity, students follow steps similar to those in the Ship Canals investigation. Students use data about canals to draw a graph and write an equation that shows the relationship between miles and kilometers.

TI-Navigator allows you to send the canal data to student calculators, and for students to send back their equations. This activity also uses Screen Captures and Quick Polls to help you evaluate student understanding.

Activity Time: 20–30 minutes

PREREQUISITES AND MATERIALS

Use this activity only if students are familiar with how to use formulas in a list, create a scatter plot, graph equations, and trace on their graphing calculators.

If students are not familiar with how to use the TABLE function on the graphing calculator, you'll need to tell them how to do this.

You will need the TI-Navigator activity file **2-4 Ship Canals.act,** lists **2-4_L1.8xl** and **2-4_L2.8xl,** and one copy per student of the Student Worksheet provided with this activity.

RUNNING THE ACTIVITY

For help logging in, see the Tip Sheet.

1. On the TI-Navigator teacher computer home screen, click the **Begin Class** button and ask students to log in on their calculators.

2. Instruct students to work through Steps 1 and 2 of the Ship Canals investigation. As they do this, send the data program to their calculators for Step 3. To do this, click the *Send to Class* icon, select the files **2-4_L1.8xl** and **2-4_L2.8xl,** and click **Next.** Click the *Class* icon, check "Force send to students now," and Click **Finish.** (*Note:* If you want students to have experience entering data into calculator lists by hand, then skip this step.) When student calculators show "TRANSFERS COMPLETE," students should press BACK ([ZOOM]) and select 4: EXIT APP.

For help with Screen Captures, see the Tip Sheet.

3. As students work on Step 4, do Screen Captures to check for student understanding on how to use list operations to create list L3.

For help with Quick Polls, see the Tip Sheet.

4. When students have completed Step 4, instruct them to re-enter NavNet, then do a Quick Poll set to "Open Response" and have students enter their rounded L3 values. Check for possible answers of 0.6, which means they computed the ratio L1/L2 or entered the data into lists in the reverse order.

Note that students
must be in NavNet in
order to respond to
Quick Polls.

5. When students have completed Step 5, do two Quick Polls set to "Open Response" for the lengths of the Suez Canal and Trollhätte Canal. During each of the Quick Polls, pause them (click **Pause Poll**) to discuss any interesting values and have students explain how they got their values, especially for the Trollhätte Canal.

6. As students work on Step 6, click the *Activity Center* icon, and choose **File | Load | Load Activity Settings** and load the activity settings file **2-4 Ship Canals.act.** Click the Graph-Equation tab. Instruct students to re-enter NavNet if they are not already there, and select 1: ACTIVITY CENTER. Click the **Start Activity** button and instruct students to send their equations. Check for student understanding and discuss student results.

7. As students work on Steps 7–9, do Screen Captures to check for student understanding on how to find the lengths of the canals using the equation, how to graph equations on the calculator, how to trace values, and how to use the table function.

Q1 Ask students why the graph passes through the origin. [Because 0 km = 0 mi.]

8. For Step 10, use the Activity Center to look at the table of values for the lengths of the missing canals. To load the lists of the data, choose **File | Load | Load Lists** and load the list files **2-4_L1.8xl** and **2-4_L2.8xl.** Click the **List-Graph** tab within the Activity Center. To see the data points, click the **Configure Plots** button and the "Plot Options" window will appear. Select the **Data Set** you want from the pull-down menu and select L1 for **Plot 1** in the **X-List** pull-down menu, and select L2 in the **Y-List** pull-down menu. In the pull-down menu to the right of the *x*-values, select the equation. Scroll down to look at the appropriate values. Click **OK.**

Q2 Discuss with students where the length of the Suez Canal would be in the table and where the length of the Trollhätte Canal would be, and why.

9. When students finish the investigation, do a Quick Poll set to "Multiple Choice A Thru D" to poll students' responses to Step 11. (Instruct students to re-enter NavNet if they have exited it.) Write these choices on the board:

A: Graph

B: Calculating with a Rate

C: Equation

D: Table

Using the results, discuss with students which method they prefer and why.

Activity 2.5

This activity consists of two parts. Each part is independent, so you can choose to do one or both. The first portion of the activity is a warm-up enhanced by TI-Navigator, in which students work through Lesson 2.4 Exercise 7. In the second portion you'll use TI-Navigator to support students as they work through the Speed versus Time investigation. You'll first send students the program they need to perform the investigation. Then you'll use TI-Navigator as a tool to facilitate groups reporting their findings.

Activity Time: Part I: 10–15 minutes; Part II: 30–40 minutes

PREREQUISITES AND MATERIALS

For Part I, you will need the TI-Navigator activity file **2-5 Ex7 Hmwk Check.act.** For Part II, you'll need the TI-Navigator activity file **2-5 Speed vs Time.act,** the calculator program **INVERSE.8xp,** and the materials listed in the Teacher's Edition.

In Part II of this activity, students use a CBR and run a program with their graphing calculators. If students are not familiar with this technology, you can modify the activity by sending students sample data as described.

SETTING UP THE EXERCISE

From the TI-Navigator teacher computer home screen, click the *Activity Center* icon. Choose **File | Load | Load Activity Settings** and load the activity settings file **2-5 Ex7 Hmwk Check.act.**

Click the **List-Graph** tab within the Activity Center.

RUNNING THE EXERCISE

Part I: First, as a warm-up activity, students will work through Lesson 2.4 Exercise 7 with the enhancement of TI-Navigator.

For help logging in, see the Tip Sheet.

1. Click the **Begin Class** button. Ask students to log in on their calculators and go to the Activity Center. Click **Start Activity.** Students will see two empty lists.

2. Tell students to read through Exercise 7 on page 119 of *Discovering Algebra.* Instruct them to write out the table of values by looking at the graph, and then enter this data into the calculator lists and send the lists.

3. Once all students have sent their data, click **Stop Activity.**

4. Check for interesting data, and discuss possible reasons why the data is a scatter plot and what could cause the interesting data.

5. Instruct students to work on part b of the exercise and develop their equations. As they do this, you'll reconfigure the activity to receive the student equations. To do this, select "Equations" from the **Contribute** pull-down menu and click **Configure.** The "Configure Calculators for Activity" window will appear. Under the **Main Settings,** choose 1 for "Number of equations per student." Check all three options for "Let students view graphs of equations," "Let students resubmit equations," and "Send current graph contents as background." Under the **Students Start with** section, select "Empty equations." Click **OK.** In the Activity Center, click the **Graph-Equation** tab.

6. Click the **Start Activity** button and ask students to send their equations.

7. Once all students have sent their equations, click **Stop Activity** and discuss any interesting equations. Also ask students to explain how they developed their equations.

8. Have the class decide on the best representative equation to use to finish the exercise.

9. Instruct students to exit the Activity Center and continue with parts c–e of the exercise.

10. Instruct students to re-enter NavNet. For parts c–e, do three Quick Polls set to "Open Response" and have students enter their answers. Check for any misunderstandings.

Part II: In the next portion of the activity, students follow steps similar to those in the Speed versus Time investigation. Students will use a CBR to collect data measuring their walking speed for a fixed-length course.

TI-Navigator allows you to send the calculator program INVERSE to student calculators, and students can send back their group data and equations. As students work through the investigation, you might also use Screen Captures and Quick Polls to help you evaluate student understanding.

> For help with Screen Captures and Quick Polls, see the Tip Sheets.

1. If students are not already logged in to NavNet, have them log in now.

2. Send the calculator program INVERSE to student calculators. To do this, click the *Send to Class* icon, select the file **INVERSE.8xp,** and click **Next.** Click the Class icon, check "Force send to students now," and click **Finish.**

3. Instruct students to exit NavNet and work through the Speed versus Time investigation.

Note: If you do not have a motion sensor, you can have students type the sample data below into their lists.

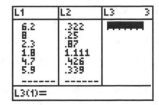

When students complete the investigation, you'll use TI-Navigator to facilitate groups reporting their findings. Steps 4–9 describe how to do this.

4. When students are almost done with the investigation, prepare for groups to report their findings. To do this, click the *Activity Center* icon on the TI-Navigator teacher computer home screen. Choose **File | Load | Load Activity Settings** and load the activity settings file **2-5 Speed vs Time.act.** Click the **List-Graph** tab within the Activity Center. When you are ready, click **Start Activity.**

5. Assign one student per group to be the group reporter, who will submit the group's lists and equations. Instruct the reporters to re-enter NavNet, enter *total time* data into L1 and *average speed* data into L2, and press SEND ([Y=]). When all groups have sent their data, click **Stop Activity.**

Q1 Every group's data will be on the computer screen. To distinguish an individual group's data, highlight the reporter's data on the left side of the screen and their data will turn blue on the screen. Ask the class to analyze the similarities and differences between the groups' data and discuss what could cause these results.

6. Reconfigure the activity to receive student equations. To do this, select "Equations" from the **Contribute** pull-down menu, and click **Configure.** The "Configure Calculators for Activity" window will appear. Under the **Main Settings,** choose 1 for "Number of equations per student." Check all three options for "Let students view graphs of equations," "Let students resubmit equations," and "Send current graph contents as background." Under the **Students Start with** section, select "Empty equations." Click **OK.** In the Activity Center, click the **Graph-Equation** tab.

7. Click **Start Activity** again, and instruct the reporters to send their equations.

8. To check each individual group's data with their equations, click the **List-Graph** tab, highlight all the student data on the left side of the Activity Center, and click

the **Hide** button at the bottom of the screen (or press Ctrl-H). Then highlight one reporter's data and click the **Show** button (or press Ctrl-S). Click the **Graph-Equation** tab and show the same reporter's equation by doing a similar hiding/showing process.

Q2 As a class, discuss how well each group's equation fits their data. You may wish to have reporters resubmit modified equations based on class input.

9. Once all groups have reported out, discuss what the inverse equation is in general and what it is for this situation.

EXPLORE MORE

Do Example A as a class by sending students the data and having them find and submit equations.

Activity 3.2

This activity is intended to prepare students for the On the Road Again investigation. It asks questions similar to Steps 1–6 of the investigation, but there is only one car involved, so it is simpler.

TI-Navigator is used to assist students in sharing data, and see equations that classmates use to fit the data gathered.

Activity Time: 10–15 minutes

PREREQUISITES AND MATERIALS

You will need the TI-Navigator activity file **3-2 Intro to Linear Plots.act** and the Student Worksheet that accompanies this activity.

SETTING UP THE ACTIVITY

From the TI-Navigator teacher computer home screen, click the *Activity Center* icon. Choose **File | Load | Load Activity Settings** and load the activity settings file **3-2 Intro to Linear Plots.act.**

Click the **List-Graph** tab within the Activity Center.

RUNNING THE ACTIVITY

This activity uses the idea of recursion from Lesson 3.1 to model the location of a moving car, and develops the idea of a linear plot. In the Student Worksheet, students answer questions similar to those they will encounter in the investigation.

1. Give students the Student Worksheet that accompanies this activity. Read through the problem with students. Have students complete questions 1–4, and discuss the answers as a class.

2. To complete question 5, assign students minute values that they'll enter into L1 and L2. One way of doing this is to give each group a card with the time values they are responsible for contributing; the 26 values needed are in the table on the Student Worksheet. Have students complete question 5, finding distance values corresponding to each time value they're given.

For help logging in, see the Tip Sheet.

3. On the TI-Navigator teacher computer home screen, click the **Begin Class** button. Ask students to log in on their calculators and go to the Activity Center. In the Activity Center, click the **Start Activity** button. Students will receive two empty lists. Have students enter their ordered pairs, with time values in L1 and distance values in L2, and press SEND ([Y=]). After all students have contributed their points, click **Stop Activity.**

4. Click **Configure Plots** and the "Plot Options" window will appear. Select L1 for the Plot 1 X-List, and L2 for the Plot 1 Y-List. Click **OK.** Students' points will be plotted. If there are any points that look incorrect, discuss. You can delete these points by clicking the coordinates in the column on the left and pressing the Delete key on your computer keyboard.

For help with Quick Polls, see the Tip Sheet.

5. Have students answer questions 6–9, and discuss the results as a class. You might do Quick Polls for answers to questions 7 and 8, and any additional questions you want to ask. (Students will need to be in NavNet to answer Quick Polls.)

6. Students should now begin work on the On the Road Again investigation. Take Screen Captures as students work to monitor progress and understanding of recursive routine formulas.

STUDENT WORKSHEET ANSWERS

1. 1.1 min/mi

2. 5.5 mi

3. Multiply the time elapsed by 1.1.

4. {0, 0} ENTER {ANS(1) + 1, ANS(2) + 1.1} ENTER; The first entry gives time in minutes, and the second entry gives distance from Flint in miles.

5.

Time (min)	Distance from Flint (mi)	Time (min)	Distance from Flint (mi)
0	0	100	110
1	1.1	110	121
2	2.2	120	132
5	5.5	130	143
10	11	140	154
20	22	150	165
30	33	160	176
40	44	170	187
50	55	180	198
60	66	190	209
70	77	200	220
80	88	210	231
90	99	220	242

6. The points form a line.

7. Yes. The car is continuously traveling, so you can determine its distance between whole minutes. At 4.5 minutes, the family has traveled 4.95 mi.

8. After 200 min

9. {0, 0} [ENTER] {ANS(1) + 1, ANS(2) + 1.2} [ENTER]; The family starts at 0 min and 0 mi. For every minute added, 1.2 miles are added (because 72 mi/h = 1.2 mi/min). This pattern will also produce a linear plot.

A family drives a pickup truck north from Flint, heading for the Mackinac Bridge, which is 220 miles away. They drive at a constant rate of 66 mi/h.

1. What is the rate of the car in miles per minute (mi/min)?

2. What is the family's distance from Flint after five minutes?

3. How can you find the family's distance from Flint at any given time in minutes?

4. What recursive routine can you use to find the distance from Flint at any time?

5. Your teacher will assign you several minute values. Find the distance from Flint at each of these time values. Log in to NavNet, and enter your time and distance values into lists L1 and L2.

Time (min)	Distance from Flint (mi)	Time (min)	Distance from Flint (mi)
0		100	
1		110	
2		120	
5		130	
10		140	
20		150	
30		160	
40		170	
50		180	
60		190	
70		200	
80		210	
90		220	

6. Your teacher will display a plot of (*time, distance*) data, which shows your data points and those entered by other students in your class. What pattern is formed?

7. Each ordered pair represents a time in minutes and a location in miles. Does it make sense to ask a question like, "How far from Flint is the family after four and a half minutes?" If so, what is the answer?

8. At what time does the family reach the Mackinac Bridge?

9. How would the calculator routine change if the family drove at a rate of 72 mi/h? Write your new routine and identify the real-world meaning of the numbers in the routine. Would you expect this pattern to also produce a linear graph?

Now you'll begin working on the On the Road Again investigation. You've already explored the motion of the pickup truck. Many of the questions you'll see in the investigation are similar to those you answered in this activity.

Activity 3.5

This activity consists of three parts. Each part is independent, so you can choose to do any combination of the parts. The first portion of the activity is a warm-up enhanced by TI-Navigator, in which students work through Lesson 3.4 Exercise 10. In the second portion, you'll use TI-Navigator to assess student comprehension as they work through the Wind Chill investigation. In the third portion, students use the program INOUT to practice writing equations to fit data.

Activity Time: Part I: 10–15 minutes; Part II: 20–30 minutes; Part III: 10–20 minutes

PREREQUISITES AND MATERIALS

For Part I, you will need the TI-Navigator activity file **3-5 Ex10 Hmwk Check.act.**

For Part II, you will need the TI-Navigator activity file **3-5 Wind Chill.act** and list files **3-5_L1.8xl** and **3-5_L2.8xl.**

For Part III, you will need the program **INOUT.8xp** and the Student Worksheet provided with this activity.

SETTING UP THE ACTIVITY

On the TI-Navigator teacher computer home screen, click the *Activity Center* icon. Choose **File | Load | Load Activity Settings** and load the activity settings file **3-5 Ex10 Hmwk Check.act.**

Click the **Graph-Equation** tab within the Activity Center.

RUNNING THE ACTIVITY

Part I: As a warm-up activity, students will work through Lesson 3.4 Exercise 10 with the enhancement of TI-Navigator.

For help logging in, see the Tip Sheet.

1. On the TI-Navigator home screen, click the **Begin Class** button. Ask students to log in on their calculators and go to the Activity Center. In the Activity Center, click the **Start Activity** button. Students will see three empty equations.

2. Tell students to study the chart in Exercise 10 on page 184 of *Discovering Algebra*. Instruct them to write equations for parts a–c.

3. Instruct the students to enter the equation for biking (a) into Y1, swimming (b) into Y2, and jogging (c) into Y3, then send their equations by pressing SEND ([Y=]).

4. Once all students have sent their equations, click **Stop Activity.**

5. Check the equations for understanding and discuss any interesting equations.

6. For part d, do Quick Polls set to "Open Response" and have students enter their answers. Check for any misunderstandings.

Part II: In the next portion of the activity, students follow steps similar to those in the Wind Chill investigation. Students will investigate the relationship between temperature and wind chill to explore the concept of rate of change and its connections to tables, scatter plots, recursive routines, equations, and graphs.

This TI-Navigator activity describes how to focus on formative assessment of student understanding throughout the investigation. Students are exposed to some new concepts in this investigation, including data that is graphed outside the first quadrant, and two-variable data that do not have consecutive or evenly spaced input values. This activity describes how to use Screen Captures and Quick Polls to help you evaluate student understanding.

Also, with TI-Navigator, you can send the wind chill data lists to students, and students can send back their equations.

1. If students are not already logged in, have them do so.

For help logging in, see the Tip Sheet.

2. Before students start the investigation, send the data lists to student calculators. To do this, click the *Send to Class* icon, select the list files **3-5_L1.8xl** and **3-5_L2.8xl,** and click **Next.** Click the *Class* icon, check "Force send to students now," and click **Finish.** (*Note:* You may prefer to have students practice entering data by hand. If so, skip this step.) Have students begin work on Steps 1–5 of the investigation.

For help with Screen Captures, see the Tip Sheet.

3. As students work on Step 2, take a Screen Capture of student calculators to see if they are using an appropriate viewing window. This is a good opportunity to discuss how this window is different from graphs that the students have worked with before. (It includes negative values on the axes.)

For help with Quick Polls, see the Tip Sheet.

4. For Step 3, do a Quick Poll set to "Open Response" and have students enter their recursive routines. (Students will need to be logged in to NavNet to respond to Quick Polls.) Have students try each other's routines to check for accuracy.

5. For Step 4, do a Quick Poll set to "Open Response" and have students enter their rate of change. Discuss any interesting values and have students explain how they calculated their rate of change.

6. As students work on Step 5 of the investigation, click the *Activity Center* icon. If your class did Part I of this activity, choose **Edit | Clear Activity Data.** Now choose **File | Load | Load Activity Settings** and load the activity settings file **3-5 Wind Chill.act.** To load the lists of the data, choose **File | Load | Load Lists** and load the list files **3-5_L1.8xl** and **3-5_L2.8xl.** (Hold the Ctrl key to select more than one list.) To see the data points, click the **List-Graph** tab. Click the **Configure Plots** button and the "Plot Options" window will appear. Select L1 for the Plot 1 X-List, and L2 for the Plot 1 Y-List. Click **OK.** Click the **Graph-Equation tab.**

7. When students complete Step 5 of the investigation, click **Start Activity.** Instruct students to re-enter NavNet and send their equations. Check for student understanding and discuss results. Ask how the rule of the recursive routine appears in the equations.

8. Have students finish Steps 6–8 of the investigation, then discuss answers.

Part III: In Lesson 3.5 Exercise 4, students use the program INOUT to practice writing equations to match data. This program can be sent to students using TI-Navigator. A Student Worksheet is provided to help students organize their work as they use the program.

1. Pass out copies of the Student Worksheet, one per student. Use TI-Navigator to send the INOUT program. (This process is described in Step 2 of Part II of this activity.) If needed, explain to students how to run a program. Model using the program once, using TI-SmartView™ or an overhead graphing calculator projection screen.

2. You might use Screen Captures to check student progress.

INOUT PROGRAM

In this program, you write a linear rule or expression that links a set of input values to their corresponding output values. Execute the program and choose a level of difficulty, then guess a rule that will give the given output value for each input value. If you make an incorrect guess, the program displays your results and allows you to try again. In the beginning, enter your guess in the form $a + b * L1$, where a is the starting value, b is the recursive rule, and $L1$ is the input list.

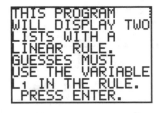  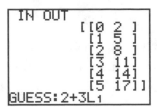 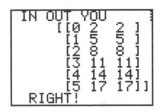

1. Run the program and play the "EASY" level four times. Each time you play, write down the output values and the equation you used to get the values in the table.

In	Out
0	
1	
2	
3	
4	
5	

Eqn:

In	Out
0	
1	
2	
3	
4	
5	

Eqn:

In	Out
0	
1	
2	
3	
4	
5	

Eqn:

In	Out
0	
1	
2	
3	
4	
5	

Eqn:

2. Run the program and play the "MEDIUM" level four times. Each time you play, write down the input and output values and the equation you used to get the values in the table.

In	Out

Eqn:

In	Out

Eqn:

In	Out

Eqn:

In	Out

Eqn:

3. Run the program and play the "HARD" level four times. Each time you play, write down the output values and the equation you used to get the values in the table.

In	Out

Eqn:

In	Out

Eqn:

In	Out

Eqn:

In	Out

Eqn:

In this activity sequence, students follow steps similar to those in Lesson 3.7 Activity Tying Knots. Students will explore the relationship between the number of knots in a rope and the length of the rope and write an equation to model this data.

TI-Navigator allows students to report out their findings by sending their data and equations.

Activity Time: 20–30 minutes

PREREQUISITES AND MATERIALS

Use this activity only if students are familiar with entering equations and data into lists with their graphing calculators.

You will need the TI-Navigator activity file **3-7 Tying Knots.act** and the materials listed in the Teacher's Edition.

SETTING UP THE ACTIVITY

On the TI-Navigator teacher computer home screen, click the *Activity Center* icon. Choose **File | Load | Load Activity Settings** and load the activity settings file **3-7 Tying Knots.act.**

Click the **List-Graph** tab within the Activity Center.

RUNNING THE ACTIVITY

For help logging in, see the Tip Sheet.

1. Have students work through Activity Tying Knots. When groups finish the activity, go to the TI-Navigator home screen and click **Begin Class.** Assign one student per group to be the group reporter. Ask the reporters to log in on their calculators and go to the Activity Center.

2. Click the *Activity Center* icon. Click **Start Activity.** Students will see two empty lists. Instruct the student reporters to enter *Number of knots* into L1 and *Length of knotted rope (cm)* into L2, and press SEND ([Y=]) to send the data. (If students gathered data on more than one rope, have them choose only one to report on now.)

3. Once all reporters have sent their data, click **Stop Activity.** Then click the *Zoom Stat* icon to see all the data. (The *Zoom Stat* icon is at the right end of the uppermost row of buttons and icons in the Activity Center.)

4. Every group's data will be displayed on the screen. To highlight an individual group's data, select the group reporter's data on the left side of the screen and their plotted data will turn blue on the graph.

Q1 Discuss the similarities and differences among various groups' data, and what might cause them.

5. Reconfigure the activity to receive student equations. To do this, go to **Contribute** and select "Equations" from the pull-down menu. Click the **Configure** button, and the "Configure Calculators for Activity" window will appear. Under the **Main Settings,** choose 1 for "Number of equations per student," and check all three options: "Let students view graphs of equations," "Let students resubmit equations," and "Send current graph contents as background." Under the **Students Start with** section, select "Empty equations." Click **OK.** In the Activity Center, click the **Graph-Equation** tab.

6. Click **Start Activity** and instruct the reporters to enter their equations and press SEND ([Y=]). Once all reporters have sent their data, click **Pause Activity.**

7. To check each individual group's data with their equations, click the **List-Graph** tab, highlight all the student data on the left side of the Activity Center, and click the **Hide** button at the bottom of the screen (or press Ctrl-H). Then highlight one reporter's data and click the **Show** button (or press Ctrl-S). Click the **Graph-Equation** tab and show only the same reporter's equation by performing a similar process (hiding all equations, then showing only the desired equation).

Q2 As a class, discuss how well each group's equation fits their data. If you like, have the class instruct the reporter to make modifications to their initial equation, and have the reporter resubmit a modified equation. (You'll need to click **Resume Activity.**)

8. If you see any unusual or interesting data or graphs, ask those groups to explain their process.

For help with Quick Polls, see the Tip Sheet.

9. For Steps 6–8, do Quick Polls set to "Open Response" and have students submit their answers. Discuss why results are different.

Q3 Discuss Steps 9 and 10. Consider these questions:
- Does the thickness of the rope affect whether the graph crosses the x-axis? Does it affect the real-world meaning of the x-value of the intersection point?
- Does the type of knot affect whether the graph crosses the x-axis? Does it affect the real-world meaning of the x-value of the intersection point?

In this activity, students follow steps similar to those in the Lesson 4.1 Example. TI-Navigator allows students to move their own coordinate point in real time to explore slope triangles. The activity concludes with several Quick Poll questions that help you evaluate student understanding.

Activity Time: 40–50 minutes

PREREQUISITES AND MATERIALS

You will need the TI-Navigator activity files **4-1 Slope Triangle.act** and **4-1 Slope Exploration.act.**

SETTING UP THE ACTIVITY

On the TI-Navigator teacher computer home screen, click the *Activity Center* icon. Then choose **File | Load | Load Activity Settings** and load the activity settings file **4-1 Slope Triangle.act.**

RUNNING THE ACTIVITY

Have students do the Points and Slope investigation. When they are finished, begin this activity.

For help logging in, see the Tip Sheet.

1. Go to the TI-Navigator home screen and click the **Begin Class** button. Ask students to log in on their calculators and go to the Activity Center.

In this activity's settings your students have a Step Size of 0.5. That is, their cursors move 0.5 unit every time they press an arrow key on their calculators.

2. Go to the Activity Center and click the **Start Activity** button. Students will see a picture of a coordinate grid with a line segment and two points. Explain to students that they have control over a point in the plane. As students move their points, you'll see the points spread out over the plane. Let them explore how their points move, then click the **Pause Activity** button.

3. Select **View | Individualize Student Cursors.** This will replace the generic cursors with icons that are unique for each student. (If there is a check next to this option in the pull-down menu, it is already selected.) You may also wish to select **View | Show Student Names.** Then, when you position your mouse over a cursor, you will see the coordinates of the cursor and the Display Name of the student to whom it belongs. Be conscious, though, about allowing students the freedom to explore anonymously. Click **Resume Activity.**

4. Instruct students to move to the point $(1, 7)$. Once every individual cursor is at $(1, 7)$, click **Pause Activity.** Tell students that when you resume the activity, they will move to the point $(6, 4)$ by following the orange arrows, and they'll count

how many units they move horizontally and vertically. (*Note:* The cursors move in increments of 0.5 unit, so observe carefully to ensure that students count properly.) Click **Resume Activity,** and allow students to move and count the lengths. Once all the students have their cursors in place at the coordinate (6, 4), click **Pause Activity.** (*Note:* Students will be tempted to not follow the arrows, so you may have to make a couple of attempts by pausing and resuming the activity with the students going back to their original position.)

For help with Quick Polls, see the Tip Sheet.

Q1 Ask students to use their horizontal and vertical distances to calculate the slope between the points (1, 7) and (6, 4). Do a Quick Poll set to "Open Response" and have students submit their slopes with a "+" sign to indicate moving right and a "−" sign to indicate moving down. (For example, down 10 and right 4 would be "−10/+4.") Discuss any unusual results and emphasize the use of the positive and negative signs for direction. When you are done with the Quick Poll, close the window.

5. Tell students that they'll now move from (6, 4) to (1, 7) following the purple arrows, and calculate the slope. Click **Resume Activity,** and have students move between the points and calculate the horizontal and vertical distances.

Q2 Again, have students use their horizontal and vertical distances to calculate the slope between the points. Do a Quick Poll set to "Open Response" and have students submit their slopes with a "+" sign to indicate moving up and a "−" sign to indicate moving left. Again, discuss any unusual results and discuss how the slope values have reversed + and − signs, due to following the orange arrows rather than the purple arrows.

Q3 Discuss whether the slope of the line is different if the slope is represented by +3/−5 or −3/+5.

6. You may want to introduce the slope formula at this time and discuss the change in y-values and the change in x-values between the starting and ending points.

Now students will further practice calculating slope using slope triangles.

7. Select **Edit | Clear Activity Data.** Choose **File | Load | Load Activity Settings** and load the activity settings file **4-1 Slope Exploration.act.** Click **Start Activity.** Display several lines and have students move along a slope triangle to find the slopes. To do this, first cover the projector display so the students cannot see the lines that you are entering. Click the **Graph-Equation** tab. On the right side of the screen, enter equations into the Y= box and click **Add.** A green line will appear for each equation you add. You might use equations such as $y = 2x$, $y = 1/3x$, $y = -4x + 4$, and $y = 0.5x + 2$. You can graph all the lines at once and have the students graph them on paper and move their cursors on the screen to trace the slope triangles

for each equation, or you can do one equation at a time. Click the **Graph** tab. Do a Quick Poll set to "Open Response" and have students submit their slopes with a "+" sign to indicate moving up or right and a "−" sign to indicate moving left or down. You can continue with other equations until you think the students have a good feel for slope triangles.

In the remainder of this activity, students will discover what lines with positive, negative, zero, and undefined slopes look like. Be sure to select **Edit | Clear Activity Data** now and after each of steps 8 through 14. You may also wish to click **Pause Activity** after each of these steps, then click **Resume Activity** when you're ready to continue.

8. To investigate positive slope, have students move their cursors and form a line with slope 1 that passes through the origin. Remind them that they cannot share the same point with anybody else in the class. It will take a while for students to organize themselves as a class. Once they have formed the line, discuss what they notice about the x- and y-values. Do a Quick Poll set to "Open Response" to have students submit the equation of the line. Click the **Graph-Equation** tab, enter the equation $y = x$ in the Y= box, and click **Add** to graph it. Click the **Graph** tab.

9. Next, have students form a line passing through the origin, with slope $\frac{1}{4}$. Once they have formed the line, do a Quick Poll set to "Open Response" and ask students to submit the equation of the line. Click the **Graph-Equation** tab, enter the equation $y = \frac{1}{4}x$ into the Y= box, and click **Add.** Discuss the steepness of the line compared to the line $y = x$.

10. Next, have students form a line passing through the origin, with slope 4 (the slope triangle will go up 4 units and over 1 unit). Once they have formed the line, do a Quick Poll set to "Open Response" and ask students to submit the equation of the line. Click the **Graph-Equation** tab, enter the equation $y = 4x$ into the Y= box, and click **Add.** Discuss the steepness of the line compared to the lines $y = x$ and $y = \frac{1}{4}x$.

11. Have students graph the three equations $y = x$, $y = \frac{1}{4}x$, and $y = 4x$ on graph paper, drawing the slope triangle for each equation.

12. To investigate negative slope, instruct students to form a line passing through the origin, in which the y-value of their point is the opposite of their x-value. Do a Quick Poll set to "Open Response" and ask students to submit the equation of the line. Have students graph other lines with negative slope, such as $y = -\frac{1}{3}x$ and $y = -3x$, until you feel that they are comfortable with comparing slopes of negative lines.

13. To investigate zero slope, instruct students to form a line for which the y-values are all 3 (that is, a horizontal line that passes through $(0, 3)$), in which the change in y is 0 but the change in x can be any number.

14. To investigate undefined slope, instruct students to form a line for which the x-values are all -4 (that is, a vertical line that passes through $(-4, 1)$), in which the change in y is any number but the change in x is 0.

Q4 Do Quick Polls set to "True False" and have students respond either "True" or "False" to the following statements. (*Note:* Either cover the projection device or move the Quick Poll window down so students cannot see each other's responses as they come in.) Discuss student responses and review concepts as needed.

- A line that goes up from left to right has a positive slope. [True.]

- A horizontal line has undefined slope. [False.]

- A line that is vertical through the x-axis has undefined slope. [True.]

- A line that goes down from left to right has negative slope. [True.]

Q5 Do Quick Polls set to "Open Response" and have students respond to the following questions. Discuss student responses and review concepts as needed.

- What is the slope of the line that passes through $(2, 4)$ and $(4, 6)$? [1]

- What is the slope of the line that passes through $(5, -3)$ and $(-2, -5)$? [2/7]

In this activity sequence, students follow steps similar to those in the Beam Strength investigation. TI–Navigator allows students to share their data easily and see equations that classmates use to fit the data gathered. This activity also includes Quick Poll questions and Screen Captures to evaluate student understanding.

For help with Screen Captures and Quick Polls, see the Tip Sheets.

There are many possible options in doing this investigation. One option is to follow all of the steps as they are in the book and do Screen Captures as students work through the investigation. The Screen Captures will give you a sense of how students are progressing. Another option is to ask Quick Poll questions as students work through the investigation. A third possibility is to have students report out their groups' findings. The last option is described in this activity.

Activity Time: 40–50 minutes

PREREQUISITES AND MATERIALS

You will need the TI-Navigator activity file **4-2 Beam Strength.act** and the materials listed in the Teacher's Edition for the Beam Strength investigation.

SETTING UP THE ACTIVITY

On the TI-Navigator teacher computer home screen, click the *Activity Center* icon. Choose **File | Load | Load Activity Settings** and load the activity settings file **4-2 Beam Strength.act.**

Click the **Graph** tab within the Activity Center.

RUNNING THE ACTIVITY

1. Have students work through Steps 1–12 of the Beam Strength investigation. Students should enter *Strands of Spaghetti* into L1 and *Maximum Load* into L2.

2. When students are almost done with the investigation, prepare for groups to report their findings. To do this, click the **Begin Class** button on the TI-Navigator home screen.

For help logging in, see the Tip Sheet.

3. Assign one student per group to be the group reporter, who will submit the group's lists and equations. Instruct the reporters to log in and go to the Activity Center. Click the *Activity Center* icon and click **Start Activity.** Reporters will see their lists L1 and L2 on their calculators. Ask them to press SEND ($\boxed{Y=}$). The Activity Center will display the data.

4. Once reporters have sent their data, click the *Zoom Stat* icon (at the far right end of the Activity Center toolbar) to see all the data. Click **Stop Activity.**

5. Every group's data will be displayed on the screen. Click the **List-Graph** tab. To highlight an individual group's data, select the group reporter's data on the left side of the screen, and their plotted data will turn blue on the screen. (If student names are not shown, select **View | Show Student Names.**) Discuss the similarities and differences among various groups' data, and what could cause them.

6. Reconfigure the activity to receive student equations. To do this, go to **Contribute** and select "Equations" from the pull-down menu. Click **Configure,** and the "Configure Calculators for Activity" window will appear. Under the **Main Settings,** choose 1 for "Number of equations per student." Check all three options for "Let students view graphs of equations," "Let students resubmit equations," and "Send current graph contents as background." Under the **Students Start with** section, select "Equations from calculator." Click **OK.** In the Activity Center, click the **Graph-Equation** tab.

7. Click **Start Activity.** Students will see their equation from Y1. Tell reporters to press SEND ([Y=]) to send in this equation.

Q1 Discuss the general direction of the line of best fit. Ask questions about the number of points above and below the line.

8. To check each individual group's data with their equations, click the **List-Graph** tab and highlight all the student data on the left side of the Activity Center and click the **Hide** button at the bottom of the screen (or press Ctrl-H). Then highlight one reporter's data and click the **Show** button (or press Ctrl-S). Click the **Graph-Equation** tab and have the same reporter's equation showing by doing a similar hiding/showing process.

Q2 As a class, discuss how well each group's equation fits their data. You may wish to have reporters resubmit their modified equations based on class input, or you can modify their equations by clicking on the particular equation and changing the rebound rate value.

For help with Quick Polls, see the Tip Sheet.

9. For Step 10 of the investigation, do a Quick Poll set to "Open Response" and have students enter their answers. Discuss differences.

10. For Step 11 of the investigation, do a Quick Poll set to "Open Response" and have students enter their answers. Discuss differences.

In the remaining steps, all students start with a given set of data and find a line of best fit. Groups' lines should be fairly similar, and you can discuss whether different lines are possible.

11. Select only one group's data to send to the whole class. To do this, delete all equations and delete all data except for that belonging to your chosen group.

Simply highlight all undesired data and equations and select **Edit | Delete,** and click **Yes** when asked if you are sure you want to delete the selection. Reconfigure the activity to receive lists. To do this, go to **Contribute** and select "Lists" from the pull-down menu. Click **Configure,** and the "Configure Calculators for Activity" window will appear. Under the **Students start with** section, select "Existing lists." Click **OK.** Click **Start Activity.** When the students have received the data, click **Stop Activity.**

12. Instruct students to exit NavNet and find an equation for the line of best fit. The group reporter will send in this equation, so group reporters will need to log back in. Reconfigure the Activity Center to receive equations again, as described in Steps 6 and 7.

Q3 Ask, "Do the lines follow the pattern of the points?"

Q4 Ask, "Are there an equal number of points above and below the line?"

Q5 Ask groups to use their model to predict the maximum load for beams made of 25 strands of spaghetti. To determine if groups got it correct, click the **Equation** tab. In the table of values on the right side of the screen, click the pull-down menu and select the equation(s) whose y-values you want to show. The y-values that correspond to the given x-values appear. The selected equations also appear in the blank table of values at the bottom of the screen. Enter 25 in the first row under "X." The corresponding y-value appears for each equation. You can use these values to allow students to check their answers.

In this activity, students follow steps similar to those in the investigation The Point-Slope Form for Linear Equations. TI-Navigator allows students to contribute equations in different forms and see that they all graph the same line. The activity concludes with several Quick Poll questions that help you evaluate student understanding.

Activity Time: 15–20 minutes. The first five steps of the activity can be teacher directed and take less time if needed.

PREREQUISITES AND MATERIALS

You will need the TI-Navigator activity file **4-3 Point Slope.act.** This activity file contains the data from the investigation.

Students should know how to find slope, graph equations on the calculator, set a graphing window, and use table-set and table functions on the calculator.

SETTING UP THE ACTIVITY

On the TI-Navigator teacher computer home screen, click the *Activity Center* icon. Choose **File | Load | Load Activity Settings** and load the activity settings file **4-3 Point Slope.act.**

Click the **Graph** tab within the Activity Center. Minimize the Activity Center while you do Steps 1–3 of this activity.

RUNNING THE ACTIVITY

For help logging in, see the Tip Sheet.

For help with Screen Captures, see the Tip Sheet.

To refresh Screen Captures, click **Refresh screens.**

1. Go to the TI-Navigator home screen and click the **Begin Class** button. Ask students to log in on their calculators and select 4: EXIT APP.

2. Have students work through The Point-Slope Form for Linear Equations investigation Steps 1–5. Assess progress by taking Screen Captures as they work.

Q1 As students work on Step 4, ask "What do you notice about the graphs of the two equations?" Refresh Screen Captures to check student work. Display them if needed for discussion.

Q2 As students work on Step 5, ask "What do you notice about the tables of the two equations?" Refresh Screen Captures to check student work. Display them if needed for discussion.

3. Ask students to return to NavNet. To do this, they press APPS, select NavNet, press ENTER (they will still be logged on), and select 1: ACTIVITY CENTER.

4. Enlarge the Activity Center window and click **Start Activity.** The investigation data will be sent to students, and will display in lists L1 and L2 on students' calculator screens. Click **Stop Activity.** (*Note:* It's okay if students press SEND before you stop the activity.)

Q3 Ask, "What does x represent?" [The time in seconds since the water began being heated.]

Q4 Ask, "What does y represent?" [The temperature of the water, in degrees Centigrade.]

5. Reconfigure the activity so that students will see the plots as well. To do this, click the **Configure** button. The "Configure Calculators for Activity" window will open. Under **Students start with,** select "Lists from calculator" and click **OK.** Click **Start Activity.** Students will again see L1 and L2, but they'll also see the option PLOT. To see a plot of the data, students press PLOT ([ZOOM]) and [ENTER]. They can move between lists and graph by pressing PLOT, LIST, and BACK. Click **Stop Activity.** (Again, if students send anything, it won't cause a problem.)

For help with Quick Polls, see the Tip Sheet.

6. Assign each group of students a pair of points from the data, repeating pairs if necessary. Ask students to calculate the slope between the two points, rounded to the nearest hundredth. Use a Quick Poll set to "Open Response" to collect answers. Note that the answers will not all be the same, but will be close.

Q5 Ask, "Why are the slopes between each pair of points not the same?" [Because the points don't exactly lie on a line.] "Why are the slopes pretty close?" [Because they *almost* lie on a line.]

7. Reconfigure the activity to receive student equations. To do this, go to **Contribute** at the left end of the tool bar and select "Equations" from the pull-down menu. Click the **Configure** button, and the "Configure Calculators for Activity" window will appear. In the **Main Settings** section, choose 1 for "Number of equations per student," and check options "Let students view graphs of equations" and "Send current graph contents as background." In the **Students Start with** section, select "Empty equations." Click **OK.** In the Activity Center, click the **Graph-Equation** tab.

8. Tell groups to write an equation in point-slope form that passes through their pair of points.

9. Click **Start Activity.** Students will receive a blank equation. Have them enter their equation and have *only one person* from each group press SEND to send their equation. Pressing PLOT will allow students to view a graph of their equation before sending.

10. Click **Stop Activity.** Compare groups' lines. The lines will be a little bit different from each other, because they are passing through different pairs of points, but because the data is fairly linear, all correct lines should be a good fit.

Ask a few questions to assess student understanding.

Q6 Ask, "Point-slope form can be used if you know two points on a line. What is the first step to finding the equation that goes through two points?" [Calculate the slope.]

Q7 Use Quick Polls set to "Open Response" to ask questions such as the following:

- What is the slope of $y = 2 + 5(x - 3)$? [5]

- What is one point on the line $y = 2 + 5(x - 3)$? [(3, 2). *Note:* If students enter a different point that is also on the line, discuss how these other points were found.]

- Write an equation in point-slope form for a line with slope -2 that passes through the point $(-3, 4)$. [$y = 4 - 2(x + 3)$]

In this activity, students start with a linear equation and create a series of equivalent equations, working toward an equation in intercept form. As students enter each equivalent equation, TI-Navigator graphs the equations. Each successive graph should overlay the previous one—if it doesn't, students know they've done something wrong.

This activity can be done before the Equivalent Equations investigation, to provide visual evidence that equivalent equations truly are equivalent—they produce the same graph.

Activity Time: 20–30 minutes

PREREQUISITES AND MATERIALS

You will need the TI-Navigator activity file **4-4 Equivalent.act.**

SETTING UP THE ACTIVITY

On the TI-Navigator teacher computer home screen, click the *Activity Center* icon. Choose **File | Load | Load Activity Settings** and load the activity settings file **4-4 Equivalent.act.**

Click the **Graph-Equation** tab within the Activity Center.

RUNNING THE ACTIVITY

1. On the TI-Navigator teacher computer home screen, click **Begin Class.** Ask students to log in on their calculators and go to the Activity Center.

2. On the teacher computer, return to the Activity Center and click **Start Activity.** Students will receive four empty equations: Y1, Y2, Y3 and Y4.

3. Tell students to enter the equation $y = 2(x - 3) + 4$ into Y1, and press SEND ($\boxed{Y=}$). A single line should be drawn in the Activity Center. If there are any extraneous lines, one or more students have entered the equation incorrectly. Ask students to check their equations. If they notice an error, they can correct the equation on their calculators and press SEND again. The old line will be replaced by a new one.

   > If you select **View | Show Student Names,** students' Display Names will show when you hold your cursor over a line. This may be helpful if extraneous lines appear.

   > If students are getting out of synch, you can click **Pause Activity** between each step.

4. Direct the class to enter equivalent equations into Y2 through Y4, one step at a time, working toward an equation in intercept form. Be sure they press SEND to send each equation. (*Note:* By pressing PLOT, they can see if their lines are equivalent before they send them.) Each equation should graph onto the previous one. Again, if extraneous lines appear, have students self-correct.

The successive equations should be: Y2 = $2x - 6 + 4$ and Y3 = $2x - 2$. (In some cases only three of the blank equations will be used.) Take advantage of the opportunity to discuss common mistakes that occur, and how they can be corrected.

5. Click **Stop Activity.** Highlight all equations on the right side of the screen and press **Delete** on your computer keyboard.

6. Repeat Steps 2–5 with several other equations. You might try the equations $y = -3(x + 1) - 4$, $y = \frac{2}{3}(6x + 3) - 5$, and $y = 4(-2x + 2) - (6x + 2)$.

In this activity, students follow steps similar to those in the Where Will They Meet? investigation. TI-Navigator allows students to share their data easily and see equations that classmates try to use to fit the data gathered. The activity contains several Quick Poll questions that help you evaluate student understanding.

Activity Time: 40–50 minutes. The activity time will depend on what data is used: You can gather data with a demonstration in front of the class or each group can collect their own data.

PREREQUISITES AND MATERIALS

Students need to be familiar with stat plots and graphing windows on the graphing calculator, and how to find a line of best fit.

You will need the TI-Navigator activity file **5-1 Systems of Equations.act** and the materials described in the Teacher's Edition.

SETTING UP THE ACTIVITY

On the TI-Navigator teacher computer home screen, click the *Activity Center* icon. Choose **File | Load | Load Activity Settings** and load the activity settings file **5-1 Systems of Equations.act.**

Click the **Graph** tab within the Activity Center.

If you choose to gather data in front of the class, set up the 6-meter course before class starts.

RUNNING THE ACTIVITY

In the Where Will They Meet? investigation, data is gathered for two walkers. You have two options for getting this data to students: Each group of students can perform the activity and gather their own data, or one group can demonstrate the walking in front of the class, and this data can be sent to all students. This activity as written describes how to perform the second option.

1. Ask students to do Step 1 of the investigation in their groups, then discuss the results.

2. Describe the activity scenario to students, and choose one or two students to help you gather data. Use a student's calculator to gather data as described in Steps 2–4 of the investigation. You should have Walker A's data in L3 and L4, and Walker B's data in L1 and L2.

Q1 How should the plots appear if the walkers walked away from the motion sensor at a constant rate? [The plots should show a positive slope or trend.]

Q2 What do the x-values represent? [Time in seconds.]

Q3 What do the y-values represent? [Distance from the motion sensor in meters.]

For help logging in, see the Tip Sheet.

3. Go to the TI-Navigator home screen and click the **Begin Class** button. Ask students to log in to NavNet. On the TI-Navigator home screen, click the *Collect from Class* icon. In the window that opens, click the arrow next to **LISTS** and select L1, L2, L3, and L4. (Hold the Ctrl key to select multiple lists.) Click **Next.** In the next window, select the student whose data you wish to retrieve (the calculator with which the data was gathered), and check "Force collect from students now." Click **Next.** Select where you wish to store the files, and click **Finish.**

4. Now you'll send this data to all students. Click the *Send to Class* icon. Select the files you just retrieved, and click **Next.** Select all students, check "Force send to students now," and click **Finish.**

5. Students will receive the four lists of data in L1 through L4. Instruct them to press BACK (ZOOM) and select 4: EXIT APP.

For help with Screen Captures, see the Tip Sheet.

6. Instruct students to plot (L3, L4) data for Walker A and (L1, L2) data for Walker B. Graph both scatter plots in the same window. As students work, you may wish to do Screen Captures to evaluate student progress.

Q4 Why do you think the graph has points only in the first quadrant? [Because time and distance must both be positive.]

7. Instruct students to work on Step 5 of the investigation, in which they find an equation that models the data set for each of the two walkers. Be sure that they enter the equations into Y1 and Y2.

8. As students work on investigation Step 5, click the *Activity Center* icon. Choose **File | Load Lists** and select the four lists that you saved in Step 3, then click **Load.** Now configure the plots. To do this, click the **List-Graph** tab. Click Configure Plots and the "Plot Options" window appears. Select L1 for the Plot 1 X-List and L2 for the Plot 1 Y-List. Select L3 for the Plot 2 X-List and L4 for the Plot 2 Y-List.

9. Now reconfigure the activity to receive student equations. To do this, go to **Contribute** and select "Equations" from the pull-down menu. Click the **Configure** button, and the "Configure Calculators for Activity" window will appear. In the **Main Settings** section, choose 2 for "Number of equations per student," and check all three options: "Let students view graphs of equations," "Let students resubmit equations," and "Send current graph contents as

background." In the **Students Start with** section, select "Equations from calculator." Click **OK.** In the Activity Center, click the **Graph-Equation** tab.

10. Instruct students to re-enter NavNet and go to the Activity Center.

11. Click **Start Activity.** Tell students to press SEND ([Y=]) to send in their lines of best fit.

Q5 What is the real-world meaning of the *y*-intercept? [The distance from the motion sensor at which the walkers started.]

Q6 What is the real-world meaning of the slope? [The rate of change, or the speed, at which the walkers moved away from the motion sensor.]

12. Choose two lines, one for each walker, that you think fit the data well. Hide all the other lines. To do this, you'll highlight all the equations and click **Hide.** Then highlight just the two equations you want to show, and click **Show.**

13. Click **Stop Activity** and reconfigure the activity to contribute points. To do this, go to **Contribute** and select "Points" from the pull-down menu. Click the **Configure** button, and the "Configure Calculators for Activity" window will appear. In the **Main Settings** section, choose 0 for "Number of points per student," enter 0.1 as the "Step size," and check "Display coordinates" and "Send current graph contents as background." Click **OK.**

14. Explain to students that they will have control over a point in the plane and should move their cursor to the intersection point of the two walkers' lines. Click **Start Activity.** Select **View | Individualize Student Cursors.** This will replace the generic cursors with icons that are unique for each student. (If there is a check next to this option, it is already selected.) You may also wish to select **View | Show Student Names.** Then, when you position your mouse over a cursor, you will see the coordinates of the cursor and the Display Name of the student to whom it belongs. Be conscious, though, about allowing students the freedom to explore anonymously. When students have moved to the point of intersection, click **Stop Activity.**

Q7 What is the real-world meaning of the intersection point? [The point where one walker would pass the other, if they were walking at the same time.]

Q8 How can you verify the point of intersection? [Substitute the coordinates for *x* and *y* in the equations for both lines, and check that they both result in a true statement.] (*Note:* Demonstrate this.)

Q9 Do a Quick Poll set to "Open Response" and ask "How fast did Walker A walk?" [Answers will vary depending on your line, but it should be about 1 m/s.]

For help with Quick Polls, see the Tip Sheet.

Q10 Do a Quick Poll set to "Open Response" and ask "How fast did Walker B walk?" [Answers will vary depending on your line, but it should be about 0.5 m/s.]

In the next few steps, you'll ask students to consider what happens under different conditions. These questions parallel Steps 9–11 of the investigation.

15. Reconfigure the activity to contribute one equation (as described in Step 9 of this activity). Click **Start Activity.**

Q11 Ask, "Suppose that Walker A walks faster than 1 m/s. How is the graph different? Enter an equation that causes Walker A to go faster and press SEND." [Students' equations should have a steeper slope than before.]

Q12 What happens to the point of intersection? [It moves earlier and closer than before.]

16. Click **Stop Activity.** Choose **Edit | Clear Activity Data.** Click **Start Activity.**

Q13 Ask, "Suppose that Walker A walks at the same speed and in the same direction as Walker B, but from a different starting mark. Enter an equation that matches this situation and press SEND." [Equations should have the same slope as Walker B's line, but a different *y*-intercept. All answers should be parallel.]

Q14 Ask, "What happens to the intersection point? What does this mean?" [There is no point of intersection. If two people start at different points and walk at the same speed and in the same direction, they will never meet.]

Q15 Do a Quick Poll set to "Open Response" and ask, "Suppose that two people walk at the same speed and in the same direction from the same starting mark. What does this graph look like? How many points satisfy this system of equations?" Have groups consult, and send in only one answer per group.

In this activity sequence, students use TI-Navigator's Activity Center to plot points that satisfy equations and inequalities. This helps them understand that there are many points that satisfy an equation, which lie on a line, and that there are many points that satisfy an inequality, which lie on a half-plane. This activity can be done after or in place of the Graphing Inequalities investigation. The activity concludes with several Quick Poll questions that help to solidify student understanding.

Activity Time: 20–25 minutes

PREREQUISITES AND MATERIALS

You will need one copy per student of the worksheet Graphing Inequalities Grids (found in *Discovering Algebra Teaching and Worksheet Masters*), and the TI-Navigator activity file **5-6 Graphing Inequalities.act.**

SETTING UP THE ACTIVITY

On the TI-Navigator teacher computer home screen, click the *Activity Center* icon. Choose **File | Load | Load Activity Settings** and load the activity settings file **5-6 Graphing Inequalities.act.**

Click the **Graph-Equation** tab within the Activity Center. In the Y= box on the right side of the screen, enter (one at a time) the expressions $1 + 0.5x$, $-1 - 2x$, $1 - 0.5x$, and $1 - 2x$, clicking **Add** after each one is entered. A green line will appear in the Activity Center for each equation. These lines are the lines in the investigation. Now press the Ctrl key on your computer keyboard and select all four expressions (they are now blue), and click **Hide.** Click the **Graph** tab.

RUNNING THE ACTIVITY

For help logging in, see the Tip Sheet.

1. On the TI-Navigator home screen, click the **Begin Class** button. Ask students to log in on their calculators and go to the Activity Center. On the teacher computer, return to the Activity Center and click **Start Activity.** Students will see a graph screen on their calculators. Explain to students that they have control over a point in the plane.

If it is not already selected, select **View | Individualize Student Cursors** to replace generic cursors with a unique icon for each student.

2. Instruct students to move their cursors to coordinates that satisfy the equation $y = 1 + 0.5x$, and request that no two students occupy the same point. When students have formed the line $y = 1 + 0.5x$, click **Pause Activity.** Click the **Graph-Equation** tab, highlight the expression $1 + 0.5x$ on the right side of the screen, and click **Show.** Students should see that the points are all on the line. Click the **Graph** tab again.

3. Instruct students to graph this line, $y = 1 + 0.5x$, on the first grid of the worksheet Graphing Inequalities Grid.

You can position your cursor over a point to display its coordinates. If you would rather not have student names displayed, be sure **View | Show Student Names** is not selected.

4. Now explain to students that they'll move their cursors to coordinates for which the y-values are *less than* the values on the line—that is, (x, y) values for which y is less than $1 + 0.5x$. Click **Resume Activity** and allow to students to start moving. The lower portion of the screen, below the graphed line, should be scattered with points. Click **Pause Activity**. Discuss why particular coordinates plotted satisfy the inequality $y < 1 + 0.5x$.

5. Instruct students to add "<" symbols to the first grid of their worksheet, indicating the location of points that satisfy $y < 1 + 0.5x$.

6. Tell students that they'll now move their cursors to coordinates for which the y-values are *greater than* the values on the line—that is, (x, y) values for which $y > 1 + 0.5x$. Click **Resume Activity,** allow students to move, and click **Pause Activity.**

7. Instruct students to add ">" symbols to the first grid of their worksheet, indicating the location of points that satisfy $y > 1 + 0.5x$.

8. Repeat Steps 2–7 with the inequalities $y > -1 - 2x$, $y < 1 - 0.5x$, and $y \geq 1 - 2x$. (Hide the equations not currently in use.) When you ask students to graph values that satisfy $y \geq 1 - 2x$, note whether any students move to points *on* the line. If so, point this out. If not, ask whether points on the line satisfy the inequality statement. (*Note:* Navigator cannot graph a dashed line, so you cannot more accurately graph $y < 1 + 0.5x$, as compared to $y \leq 1 + 0.5x$. Discuss the difference between dashed and solid lines with your class.)

For help with Quick Polls, see the Tip Sheet.

Q1 You may wish to conduct a few Quick Polls set to "Yes No," such as the following:

- Does the point $(0, 1)$ satisfy the inequality $y < 1 - 0.5x$? [No.]

- Does the point $(0, 1)$ satisfy the inequality $y \geq 1 - 2x$? [Yes.]

- Does the point $(0, 0)$ satisfy the inequality $y \geq 1 - 2x$? [No. Discuss what this means about the graph—the half of the plane that includes $(0, 0)$ is not shaded.]

In this activity students use TI-Navigator's Activity Center to plot points that satisfy systems of equations and inequalities.

This activity can be done after or in place of the A "Typical" Envelope investigation.

Activity Time: 20 minutes

PREREQUISITES AND MATERIALS

This activity will work best if you have also done the TI-Navigator activity for Lesson 5.6.

You will need one copy per student of the Student Worksheet that accompanies this activity, and the TI-Navigator activity file **5-7 Systems Inequalities.act.**

SETTING UP THE ACTIVITY

On the TI-Navigator teacher computer home screen, click the *Activity Center* icon. Choose **File | Load | Load Activity Settings** and load the activity settings file **5-7 Systems Inequalities.act.**

Click the **Graph-Equation** tab. Enter the expressions (e.g., "$-x - 1$") in the systems below into the Y= box on the right side of the screen, clicking **Add** after each one is entered. Press the Ctrl key on your computer keyboard and select all eight expressions, and click **Hide.** Click the **Graph** tab.

Systems of Inequalities

$y \geq -x - 1$	$y \geq 1/2x - 2$	$y \geq 3x + 1$	$y < x$
$y < 2x + 2$	$y < -4x + 1$	$y < -1/3x + 3$	$y < -2$

RUNNING THE ACTIVITY

In this activity, students move cursors in the Activity Center to first graph the solutions of one inequality, then a second inequality, and finally the region that is the solution to both inequalities simultaneously.

1. Hand out the Student Worksheet that accompanies this activity.

For help logging in, see the Tip Sheet.

2. On the TI-Navigator home screen, click the **Begin Class** button. Ask students to log in on their calculators and go to the Activity Center. On the teacher computer, return to the Activity Center and click **Start Activity.** Students will see a graph screen on their calculators. Explain to students that they have control over a point in the plane.

3. Instruct students to move their cursors to coordinates that satisfy the equation $y = -x - 1$, and request that no two students occupy the same point. When students have formed the line $y = -x - 1$, click **Pause Activity.** Click the **Graph-Equation** tab, highlight the expression $-x - 1$ on the right side of the screen, and click **Show.** Students should see that the points are all on the line. Click the **Graph** tab again.

Q1 Ask one or two students to state their coordinates, and to explain why these coordinates lie on the line. [Students should understand that a point (x, y) satisfies an equation if a true statement results when the x- and y-values are substituted into the equation.]

4. Tell students that next they'll move their cursors to coordinates that satisfy $y \geq -x - 1$. Click **Resume Activity** and wait for students to move their cursors above the graphed line. Click **Pause Activity.** Point out to students which side of the line is "shaded." (They'll use this information again shortly.)

Q2 Again, ask one or two students to state their coordinates, and explain why these coordinates satisfy the inequality. [Students should understand that a point (x, y) satisfies an inequality if a true statement results when the x- and y-values are substituted into the inequality.]

5. Next, instruct students to form the line $y = 2x + 2$ with their cursors. Click **Resume Activity,** wait for students to move, and click **Pause Activity** again. Click the **Graph-Equation** tab, highlight the expression $2x + 2$, and click **Show.** A second green line will appear, which should pass through all the student cursors.

6. Instruct students to move their cursors to coordinates that satisfy $y < 2x + 2$. Click **Resume Activity,** wait for students to move their cursors below the line and click **Pause Activity.** Again, point out which side of the line is "shaded."

7. Now, instruct students to move their cursors to a point that satisfies *both* inequalities, $y \geq -x - 1$ and $y < 2x + 2$. Click **Resume Activity.** When students have moved their cursors to the solution region, click **Pause Activity.** Discuss the results.

Q3 Ask one or two students to state their coordinates, and to explain why these coordinates satisfy the system of inequalities. [Students should understand that a point (x, y) satisfies a system of inequalities if a true statement results when the x- and y-values are substituted into both inequalities.] If no student has positioned their cursor *on* the line $y = -x - 1$, ask whether a point on that line would satisfy the system. [Yes.] Ask whether a point on the line $y = 2x + 2$ would satisfy the system. [No.]

For help with Quick Polls, see the Tip Sheet.

8. Instruct students to graph the two inequalities on their worksheets and shade the area that satisfies the system of inequalities. TI-Navigator cannot draw dashed lines, so be sure to discuss which line in the system should be graphed with a dashed line. Do a Quick Poll set to "Yes No" and ask for each line, "Should this line be graphed dashed?"

9. Repeat Steps 3–8 for the next three systems of equations given on page 46. (Hide unused equations first.) If you like, you can give students additional systems of inequalities and have students graph them on their worksheets without the use of TI-Navigator.

Graph the systems of inequalities given by your teacher on these coordinate axes.

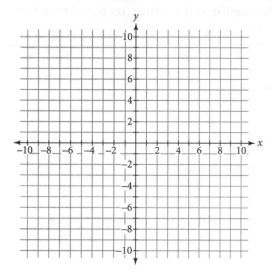
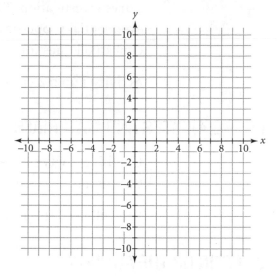
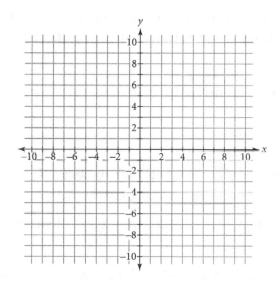
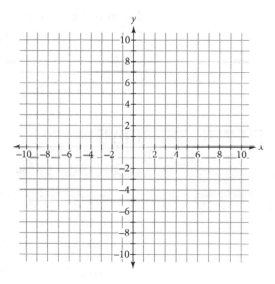
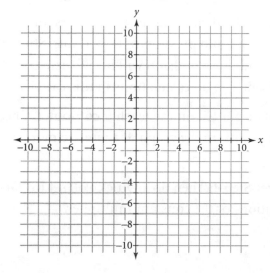
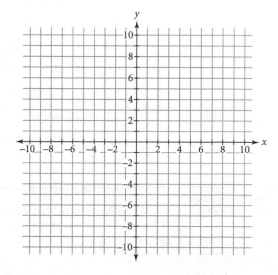

Activity 6.2

In this activity, students follow steps similar to those in the Growth of the Koch Curve investigation. TI-Navigator allows students to enter data and explore exponential properties of the Koch Curve. The activity concludes with several Quick Poll questions that help you evaluate student understanding.

Activity Time: 25 minutes

PREREQUISITES AND MATERIALS

Use this activity only if students are familiar with how to enter data into lists on their graphing calculators.

You will need the TI-Navigator activity file **6-2 Koch Curve.act.**

SETTING UP THE ACTIVITY

From the TI-Navigator teacher computer home screen, click the *Activity Center* icon. Then choose **File | Load | Load Activity Settings** and load the activity settings file **6-2 Koch Curve.act.**

Click the **List-Graph** tab within the Activity Center.

RUNNING THE ACTIVITY

For help logging in, see the Tip Sheet.

1. Go to the TI-Navigator home screen and click the **Begin Class** button. Ask students to log in on their calculators and go to the Activity Center.

2. Go to the Activity Center and click **Start Activity.** Students will see two empty lists on their calculators.

3. Instruct students to work on Steps 1–3 of the Growth of the Koch Curve investigation in their textbooks. When they have determined the lengths for Stages 0 through 3, have them enter the stage numbers into L1 and total lengths into L2 on their calculators, and press SEND ([Y=]). (*Note:* Students can enter an expression into a list, and the expression will be evaluated, so it's not necessary to leave the Activity Center to do calculations in this case.)

4. All students' data will be plotted on the teacher computer. Check that there are only four distinct points on the graph. If there are more points than this, discuss.

For help with Quick Polls, see the Tip Sheet.

5. Ask students to answer Step 4. Then do a Quick Poll set to "Open Response" to check student calculations of the constant multiplier.

6. Instruct students to do Step 5, then enter this new data into their calculator lists and send again (press [Y=]). (The activity hasn't been stopped, so students will be adding to their current lists rather than replacing data.) Again, check the graph to ensure that there are only six distinct points. Click **Stop Activity.**

Q1 When students have completed Step 6, do a Quick Poll set to "Open Response" and ask students to enter their expressions that calculate the length at Stage 2. Discuss students' equations. Note what values were chosen for the initial amount, and how equations were written in general. Look for any equations that might help illustrate the exponential properties. (For example, you might have the opportunity to discuss why $27\left(\frac{4}{3}\right)^2$ is the same as $27\left(\frac{4}{3}\right)\left(\frac{4}{3}\right)$.)

7. For Steps 7–9, do Quick Polls similar to that in Q1.

8. For Step 10, return to the Activity Center and change the settings to contribute equations. (On the left side of the tool bar, select "Equations" from the **Contribute** pull-down menu.) Click **Configure,** choose 1 for "Number of equations per student," and under **Students Start with,** select "Equations from calculator." Click **Start Activity.** Have students enter their equations and press SEND ([Y=]).

Q2 Check whether all equations pass through the six points plotted. If not, discuss.

Q3 You might ask a few additional questions, and either gather responses using Quick Poll, or simply discuss. Consider these questions:

- Are all values of x and y (whole numbers, negative numbers, decimals, and so on) meaningful in this equation? [No. Only the numbers 0, 1, 2,... make sense for the stage number, x. Only positive values are possible for length, y.]

- The graph is a smooth continuous curve. Is this an accurate representation of the (*stage, length*) values? [No. Only discrete points with whole number x-values make sense.]

- What does each part of the equation represent in terms of the Koch curve? [27 is the initial length. $\frac{4}{3}$ indicates that for each stage increase, the length grows by $\frac{4}{3}$ (because each segment is divided into three sections, then those three sections are replaced by four segments). The exponent, x, is the stage number. y is the total length for a given stage number.]

- What do the equation and graph show you about the growth of the Koch curve? [The length of the Koch curve increases without bound, and increases faster as the stage number gets larger.]

In this activity, students follow steps similar to those in the Radioactive Decay investigation. Students explore exponential data and write an equation to model this data.

TI-Navigator allows students to report their findings by sending their data and equations for display on the teacher's computer.

Activity Time: 20–30 minutes

PREREQUISITES AND MATERIALS

Use this activity only if students are familiar with entering equations and data into lists with their graphing calculators.

You will need the TI-Navigator activity file **6-7 Radioactive Decay.act** and the materials listed in the Teacher's Edition.

SETTING UP THE ACTIVITY

On the TI-Navigator teacher computer home screen, click the *Activity Center* icon. Choose **File | Load | Load Activity Settings** and load the activity settings file **6-7 Radioactive Decay.act.**

Click the **List-Graph** tab within the Activity Center.

RUNNING THE ACTIVITY

For help logging in, see the Tip Sheet.

1. Have students work through the Radioactive Decay investigation in their textbooks. When groups finish the investigation, go to the TI-Navigator home screen and click **Begin Class.** Assign one student per group to be the group reporter. Ask the reporters to log in on their calculators and go to the Activity Center.

2. Click the *Activity Center* icon. Click **Start Activity.** The reporters will see two empty lists on their calculator screens. Instruct the reporters to enter *elapsed time in years* into L1 and *number of atoms remaining* into L2, and press SEND ([Y=]). (This data was collected in Steps 1–3 of the investigation.)

3. Once all reporters have sent their data, click **Stop Activity.** Then click the *Zoom Stat* icon to see all the data. (The *Zoom Stat* icon is at the right end of the uppermost row of buttons and icons in the Activity Center.)

4. Every group's data will be displayed on the screen. To highlight an individual group's data, select the group reporter's data on the left side of the screen and their plotted data will turn blue on the graph.

Q1 Discuss the similarities and differences among various groups' data, and what might cause them.

5. Reconfigure the activity to receive student equations. To do this, go to **Contribute** and select "Equations" from the pull-down menu. Click the **Configure** button, and the "Configure Calculators for Activity" window will appear. Under the **Main Settings,** choose 1 for "Number of equations per student," and check all three options: "Let students view graphs of equations," "Let students resubmit equations," and "Send current graph contents as background." Under the **Students Start with** section, select "Empty equations." Click **OK.** In the Activity Center, click the **Graph-Equation** tab.

6. Click **Start Activity** and instruct the reporters to enter their equations and press SEND ([Y=]). Click **Stop Activity.**

7. To check each individual group's data with their equations, click the **List-Graph** tab, highlight all the student data on the left side of the Activity Center, and click the **Hide** button at the bottom of the screen (or press Ctrl-H). Then highlight one reporter's data and click the **Show** button (or press Ctrl-S). Click the **Graph-Equation** tab and show only the same reporter's equation by performing a similar process (hiding all equations, then showing only the desired equation).

Q2 As a class, discuss how well each group's equation fits their data. If you like, have the class instruct the reporter to make modifications to their initial equation, and have the reporter resubmit a modified equation.

8. If you see any unusual or interesting data or graphs, ask those groups to explain their process.

For help with Quick Polls, see the Tip Sheet.

9. For Steps 6–8, do Quick Polls set to "Open Response" and have students submit their answers. Discuss why results are different.

Q3 Consider these possibilities as you discuss Steps 11 and 12.

- Describe a connection between your angle and the numbers in your equation.

- Do a Quick Poll set to "Open Response" and have students submit their equations for Step 12 of the investigation. Ask, "What are some of the factors that might cause differences between actual data and values predicted by your equation?"

In this activity sequence, students follow steps similar to those in Lesson 6.8 Activity Bouncing and Swinging, Experiment 1: Ball Bounce. Students gather real-world data and find a model that fits it, while exploring decreasing exponential models and learning about half-life.

TI-Navigator allows you to send the calculator program needed by students to conduct the experiment, and enables students to report out their findings by sending in their data and equations.

Activity Time: 20–30 minutes

PREREQUISITES AND MATERIALS

Use this activity only if students are familiar with entering equations and data into lists with their graphing calculators.

You will need the materials required for Experiment 1: Ball Bounce, described in the Teacher's Edition; you also will need the TI-Navigator activity file **6-8 Ball Bounce.act** and the calculator program **BOUNCE.8xp.**

SETTING UP THE ACTIVITY

From the TI-Navigator teacher computer home screen, click the *Activity Center* icon. Choose **File | Load | Load Activity Settings** and load the activity settings file **6-8 Ball Bounce.act.**

Click the **List-Graph** tab within the Activity Center.

Return to the TI-Navigator teacher computer home screen, click **Begin Class** and click the *Send to Class* icon. Select the calculator program file **BOUNCE.8xp** and click **Next.** Click **Class,** check "Force send to students now," and click **Finish.**

RUNNING THE ACTIVITY

For help logging in, see the Tip Sheet.

1. Ask students to log in to NavNet on their calculators. Students will receive the BOUNCE program. Tell them to select 4: EXIT APP and work through Steps 1–4 of Activity Bouncing and Swinging Experiment 1: Ball Bounce in their textbooks. Students will use the BOUNCE program as they work on the Experiment.

2. When students are almost done with the investigation, prepare for groups to report their findings. To do this, click the *Activity Center* icon and click **Start Activity.**

3. Assign one student per group to be the group reporter, who will submit the group's lists and equations. Instruct the reporters to re-enter NavNet and go to the Activity Center. They'll see the ball bounce data they collected in L1 and L2. Tell reporters to press SEND ([Y=]) to send in this data.

4. Once reporters have sent their data, click the *Zoom Stat* icon (at the far right end of the Activity Center toolbar) to see all the data. Click **Stop Activity.**

Q1 Every group's data will be on the computer screen. To distinguish an individual group's data, highlight the reporter's data on the left side of the screen and their data will turn blue on the screen. Ask the class to analyze the similarities and differences between each group's data and the rest, and discuss what could cause these results.

5. Reconfigure the activity to receive student equations. To do this, go to **Contribute** and select "Equations" from the arrow menu. Click **Configure,** and the "Configure Calculators for Activity" window will appear. Under the **Main Settings,** choose 1 for "Number of equations per student." Check all three options for "Let students view graphs of equations," "Let student resubmit equations," and "Send current graph contents as background." Under the **Students Start with** section, select "Equations from calculator." Click **OK.** In the Activity Center, click the **Graph-Equation** tab.

6. Click **Start Activity.** Students will see their equation from Y1. Tell reporters to press SEND ([Y=]) to send in this equation.

7. To check each individual group's data with their equations, click the **List-Graph** tab and highlight all the student data on the left side of the Activity Center and click the **Hide** button at the bottom of the screen (or press Ctrl-H). Then highlight one reporter's data and click the **Show** button (or press Ctrl-S). Click the **Graph-Equation** tab and have the same reporter's equation showing by doing a similar hiding/showing process.

Q2 As a class, discuss how well each group's equation fits their data. You may wish to have reporters resubmit their modified equations based on class input, or you can modify their equations by clicking on the particular equation and changing the rebound rate value.

8. If you notice any unusual data or equations, or a particularly good fit, you may wish to discuss or have reporters present their approaches.

9. Click **Stop Activity** and instruct the students to continue working through Steps 5–7 of the Activity in the textbook. Students may exit NavNet.

For help with Screen
Captures, see the
Tip Sheet.

Q3 For Step 5, have students enter their answers on the home screen of their calculators, and do a Screen Capture of students' calculators. Conduct a class discussion on the meaning of half-life for a ball bounce in general terms.

10. For Step 6, show Screen Captures of student calculators and discuss how the various half-life values compare.

11. For Step 7, students can present their findings as you highlight their particular data and equations.

In this activity, students follow steps similar to those in the investigation A Graphic Message. TI-Navigator allows students to interactively show their answers using the Activity Center. LearningCheck files can be used as warm-ups or quick evaluation activities. The activity begins and concludes with a LearningCheck file that helps evaluate student understanding.

This activity has three parts. Part I is a LearningCheck file that reviews Lessons 7.1 through 7.3. Part II is an interactive version of the investigation A Graphic Message. Part III is a LearningCheck file that provides additional practice with the concepts of Lesson 7.4. You can do any combination of these three parts.

Activity Time: Part I: 20 minutes; Part II: 10 minutes; Part III: 20 minutes

PREREQUISITES AND MATERIALS

For Part I, you will need the LearningCheck file **7-4 Functions.edc.** For Part II, you'll need the TI-Navigator activity file **7-4 Function Graph.act** and the worksheet "A Graphic Message," provided in the *Discovering Algebra* teacher materials. For Part III, you'll need the LearningCheck file **7-4 Function Notation.edc.**

SETTING UP THE ACTIVITY

To set up Part I, on the TI-Navigator teacher computer home screen, click **Begin Class** and click the *Send to Class* icon. Select the file **7-4 Functions.edc** and click **Next.** Click the *Class* icon, check "Force send to students now," and click **Finish.**

RUNNING THE ACTIVITY

Part I: In this part of the activity, students will take an assessment on their calculators, then you'll retrieve and evaluate their answers.

For help logging in, see the Tip Sheet.

1. Ask students to log in on their calculators. They will immediately see files being transferred to their calculators. When the calculator says "TRANSFERS COMPLETE," instruct students to press BACK ([ZOOM]), then select 2: NETWORK APPS.

2. Tell students to select LearnChk by pressing [ENTER]. Students will then see an assignment list. Tell students to arrow down to Functions and press [ENTER].

3. Students should work through the assessment on their calculators. If this is the first LearningCheck assessment they've done, they'll need some time to experiment and figure out how to navigate through the file and select answers. Write these hints on the board, or distribute the Tip Sheet on page viii:

   • Select PIC or TXT to move between the picture and text for a particular question.

- Select Q or ANS to move between the question and answer for a particular question.

- Always press ENTER to select your answer. If you move to the answer but do not press ENTER, your answer will not be recorded.

- Select NEXT to move to the next question.

- You can always select MENU to see a list of options. You can go back to the previous item or see a list of items and choose which one you want. You can redo problems if you like. (In the MENU screen, answered questions have a small square next to them.)

For help with Screen Captures, see the Tip Sheet.

4. As students work through the assessment, you can take Screen Captures to view students' calculator screens and check that students are on task and making progress.

Now you'll retrieve the class data.

5. To retrieve class data, make sure all students have finished the assessment, then click the *Class Analysis* icon.

6. Click the *Collect Answer Files From Classroom Devices* icon to retrieve the data from student handhelds. A "Collect Answer Files from Class" window opens. Check "Delete Answer File from Device after Collect" and "Delete Assignment File from Device after Collect." Then click **Start Transfer.** (If some students did not take the quiz, you'll get an "External Request" message. Click **OK** and then, when all LearningCheck files have been collected, click **Stop** on the left side of the screen, where it says "External Request.")

For more information on how to use Class Analysis, see the TI-Navigator Software Tours or the TI-Navigator Reference Guide.

Answer data is collected from the student calculators and displayed in a spreadsheet. Each student's data is stored as a separate file (called a user file) with the file extension ".usf." The Class Analysis program displays all of these individual files as one spreadsheet. The data will not be lost unless the files are deleted. You can print, save, or view the data in a slide show.

You'll now display results in a slide show and discuss the results with your class.

7. In the Class Analysis window, click the *Class Results Slide Show* icon. The slide show contains each question followed by a bar chart showing the number of students who entered each answer option. The buttons at the top of the screen allow you to stop the slide show, return to the beginning, move back one slide, move forward one slide, or move to the end of the slide show.

8. Move through the slide show with students, and discuss any interesting results. Be sure to point out common mistakes and address how to avoid them.

Part II: In this portion of the activity, students can move their cursors in the Activity Center to determine function values for the given piecewise-function graph.

1. On the TI-Navigator teacher computer home screen, click the *Activity Center* icon. Choose **File | Load | Load Activity Settings** and load the activity settings file **7-4 Function Graph.act.** Click the **Graph** tab.

2. Students should have a copy of the worksheet "A Graphic Message." Tell students that they will be filling out the tables and then using the Activity Center to move to some of the answers.

Q1 Ask students to describe the domain and range of the function *f* in the graph.

Q2 Use a Quick Poll set to "Open Response" and ask, "What is the input variable called?" [Domain.]

For help with Quick Polls, see the Tip Sheet.

Q3 Use a Quick Poll set to "Open Response" and ask, "What is the output variable called?" [Range.]

3. Instruct students to select 1: ACTIVITY CENTER on their calculators.

4. Click the **Start Activity** button. Choose **View | Individualize Student Cursors.**

5. As students work through finding the values in the first table on the worksheet, have them move to the appropriate place in the Activity Center graph. For example, instruct students to first move to $f(3)$. Click **Pause Activity** and discuss as needed. Click **Resume Activity** and continue to have students move to other values on the table.

6. Before continuing to the second table, discuss and review the order of operations as needed. Remind students to do any operations inside parentheses first. Then use the graph to find the function values before doing the remaining operations. Again, have students write their answers in the table. You can use the Activity Center to move to particular function values, pausing and discussing as necessary.

Part III: Now, after students have completed the A Graphic Message investigation, you'll use a LearningCheck assessment to evaluate student understanding.

1. From the TI-Navigator teacher computer, click the *Send to Class* icon. Select the file **7-4 Function Notation.edc** and click **Next.** Click the *Class* icon, check "Force send to students now," and click **Finish.**

2. Students will see files being transferred to their calculators. When the calculator says "TRANSFERS COMPLETE," instruct students to press BACK ([ZOOM]), then select 2: NETWORK APPS.

3. Tell students to select LearnChk by pressing ENTER. Students will then see an assignment list. Tell students to arrow down to Function notation and press ENTER.

4. Students should work through the assessment on their calculators. If students are not familiar with LearningCheck assessments, write the hints given in Part I of this activity on the board, and give them plenty of time to explore.

5. As students work through the assessment, you can take Screen Captures to view students' calculator screens and check that students are on task and making progress.

6. Now you'll retrieve the class data. Do this as described in Steps 5 and 6 of Part I of this activity.

7. You'll now display results in a slide show and discuss the results with your class. Do this as described in Steps 7 and 8 of Part I of this activity.

In this activity, students use TI-Navigator's Activity Center to explore absolute value.

In Part I, students measure distance to identify the need for absolute value, and then use Quick Poll questions to solidify their understanding. In Part II, students use the Activity Center to send in their pulse rates to explore the absolute-value function.

Activity Time: Part I: 10 minutes; Part II: 20–35 minutes

PREREQUISITES AND MATERIALS

Use this activity only if students are familiar with how to enter data in lists on their graphing calculators.

For Part I, you will need the TI-Navigator activity file **7-5 Absolute Value.act.** For Part II, you will need the TI-Navigator activity file **7-5 Deviations from Mean.act.**

SETTING UP THE ACTIVITY

On the TI-Navigator teacher computer home screen, click the *Activity Center* icon. Choose **File | Load | Load Activity Settings** and load the activity settings file **7-5 Absolute Value.act.**

Click the **Graph** tab within the Activity Center.

RUNNING THE ACTIVITY

Part I: In this activity, students move cursors between images in the Activity Center to find distances.

For help logging in, see the Tip Sheet.

1. Go to the TI-Navigator home screen and click **Begin Class.** Ask students to log in on their calculators and go to the Activity Center.

2. Go to the Activity Center and click **Start Activity.** Students will see a graph screen on their calculators. Explain to students that they have control over a point in the plane.

In this activity's settings your students have a Step Size of 0.5. That is, their cursors move 0.5 unit every time they press an arrow key.

3. Choose **View | Individualize Student Cursors.** This will replace the generic cursors with icons that are unique for each student.

4. Ask students to move their cursors to the school. Once students are there, click **Pause Activity.** Now click **Resume Activity** and instruct students to move to the house. Once students are there, click **Pause Activity.**

Q1 Click the *Quick Poll* icon, set the poll to "Open Response," and click **Start Poll.** Move the Quick Poll window off the screen, so that students cannot see individual responses as they are submitted, and so that students can see the diagram on the computer screen. Ask the class, "What is the distance from the house to the school?" Have students enter their responses into the calculator and press SEND ([Y=]). When students are finished, click **Stop Poll** and raise the Quick Poll window to show the responses. Discuss the definition of absolute value at this time by asking, "Can distance ever be negative?" Close the Quick Poll window.

5. In the Activity Center, click **Resume Activity** and ask students to move to the apartment building. Click **Pause Activity.**

Q2 Click the *Quick Poll* icon, set the poll to "Open Response," click **Start Poll,** and move the window off-screen again. Ask the class, "What is the distance from the apartment building to the school?" Have students enter their responses into the calculator and press SEND ([Y=]). When students are finished, click **Stop Poll** again and raise the Quick Poll window to show the responses. Discuss as needed.

Q3 Click **Start Poll** again, move the Quick Poll window off-screen, and ask, "What is the distance from the house to the apartment building?" When students are finished, click **Stop Poll** again and raise the Quick Poll window to show the responses. Discuss as needed. Students should understand that distance is positive, regardless of the direction of movement.

6. In the Activity Center, click **Stop Activity.** Choose **Edit | Clear Activity Data.**

Part II: In this part of the activity, students will use TI-Navigator to submit their pulse rate and receive all class pulse rates into their calculators, in preparation for the Deviations from the Mean investigation.

1. On the TI-Navigator teacher computer home screen, click the *Activity Center* icon. Choose **File | Load | Load Activity Settings** and load the activity settings file **7-5 Deviation from Mean.act.** Click the **List** tab within the Activity Center to see the data.

2. If you did not do Part I of this activity, click **Begin Class** now and ask students to log in on their calculators and go to the Activity Center.

3. Click **Start Activity.** Students will see an empty list on their calculators. Ask students to take their pulse, enter their data value in the empty list, and press SEND ([Y=]).

4. When all students have submitted their data, click **Stop Activity.**

5. Now you'll combine all the students' data and send it back to them in an aggregated list. To do this, click **Configure,** select "Existing activity lists," and click **OK.**

6. Click **Start Activity** again, and students will receive the aggregated list in L1 on their calculators. Click **Stop Activity.**

7. Students can now exit the Activity Center and have full use of their calculators as they continue with Step 2 of the Investigation. To do this, students press 2nd [QUIT] and select 4: EXIT APP.

For help with Screen Captures, see the Tip Sheet.

8. As students work on Steps 2–4 of the investigation, take Screen Captures to check for progress and understanding. When students are nearing completion of these steps, reconfigure the activity to receive students' lists L2 and L3. To do this, go to **Contribute** and select "Lists" from the pull down menu. Click **Configure.** The "Configure Calculators for Activity" window will appear. Click **Create New Lists,** and the "Create New Lists" window will appear. Set the number of lists to 2, select L2 and L3, select "Group lists as a Data Set," then click **OK** to close this window. Next, click the **Configure Plots** button in the "Configure Calculators for Activity" window. For Plot 1, choose L2 for the X-List and choose L3 for the Y-List. Click **OK.** Under **Students start with,** select "Lists from calculator." Click **OK.**

9. After students have completed Steps 2–4, click **Start Activity** and instruct the students to go back into NavNet and select 1: ACTIVITY CENTER. Tell them to press SEND ([Y=]) to send their lists to the teacher computer. All students' data should be exactly the same. Discuss any different data.

10. Discuss the questions posed in Steps 4–7, using the projected Activity Center graph and student Screen Captures.

11. As students work on Step 8, graph $y = |x|$ in the Activity Center by going to the **Graph-Equation** tab and typing into the Y= box and then clicking the **Graph** tab.

12. Finish the lesson with the discussion and writing exercise in Step 10.

This activity can be used as an introduction to parabolas, prior to students completing the Graphing a Parabola investigation. TI-Navigator allows students to move points in real time to explore the parabolic function. The activity concludes with several Quick Poll questions that help you evaluate student understanding.

Activity Time: 20 minutes

PREREQUISITES AND MATERIALS

You will need the TI-Navigator activity file **7-6 Graph Parabola.act.**

SETTING UP THE ACTIVITY

From the TI-Navigator teacher computer home screen, click the *Activity Center* icon. Choose **File | Load | Load Activity Settings** and load the activity settings file **7-6 Graph Parabola.act.**

Note: You may need to change the window settings to fit the number of students you have in class. Currently, the activity center window is set for 28–30 students. If you want to change the window to accommodate more or less students, click the *Edit Window Settings* icon (the red check mark), change the X Min and X Max values to fit the number of students in your class, and square the X Max value to get the value for Y Max.

Click the **Graph** tab within the Activity Center.

RUNNING THE ACTIVITY

For help logging in, see the Tip Sheet.

1. On the TI-Navigator home screen, click the **Begin Class** button. Ask students to log in on their calculators and go to the Activity Center. On the teacher computer, go to the Activity Center and click **Start Activity.** Students will see a coordinate grid. Explain to students that they have control over a point in the plane. As students move, you'll see them spread out over the plane. Let them play a little, then click **Pause Activity.**

2. Select **View | Individualize Student Cursors.** This will replace the generic cursors with icons that are unique for each student. (If there is a check next to this option, it is already selected.) You may also wish to select **View | Show Student Names.** Then, when you position your mouse over a cursor, you will see the coordinates of the cursor and the Display Name of the student to whom it belongs. Be conscious, though, about allowing students the freedom to explore anonymously.

In this activity's settings your students have a Step Size of 0.5. That is, their cursors move 0.5 unit every time they press an arrow key.

3. Click **Resume Activity** and instruct students to move their cursors onto the x-axis such that no two are sharing the same point and no one is at the origin. Once every cursor is in position, click **Pause Activity.** Instruct students to multiply their x-value by itself (square it) and move straight up to this y-value. (For example, if a student is on the x-value 3, they'll move to (3, 9).) Click **Resume Activity.** Let the students move until their points create a parabola.

4. Once students are in position, instruct them to press MARK ([Y=]) to mark their point.

Q1 Discuss the shape that has been formed and its properties, such as symmetry. Ask students to identify the line of symmetry. Discuss how this graph is related to the relationship between the length of a side of a square and its area.

5. Click **Stop Activity** and reconfigure the activity to receive student equations. To do this, go to **Contribute** and select "Equations" from the pull-down menu. Click **Configure,** and the "Configure Calculators for Activity" window will appear. Under the **Main Settings,** choose 1 for "Number of equations per student." Check the two options for "Let students view graphs of equations," and "Send current graph contents as background." Under the **Students Start with** section, select "Empty Equations." Click **OK.**

6. Click **Start Activity** and have students submit a guess for an equation that fits the points. Click **Stop Activity.**

Q2 Discuss any unusual results and note how many students sent the correct equation.

7. Tell students to begin working on the Graphing a Parabola investigation in their textbooks.

For help with Quick Polls, see the Tip Sheet.

8. As students work on Steps 3 and 5–7, do Quick Polls set to "Open Response" to check for understanding. (Students will need to re-enter NavNet.)

9. Conduct a class discussion for Steps 8–10, referring back to the graph in the Activity Center. You can click the **Graph-Equation** tab and enter the equation $y = \text{abs}(x)$ for comparison.

In this activity, students follow steps similar to those in the Translations of Functions investigation. This activity can be used as a replacement for the investigation.

The TI-Navigator activity settings are set to mask teacher input, allowing you to project graphed functions and then have students practice writing equations to match your graph.

Activity Time: 40–50 minutes

PREREQUISITES AND MATERIALS

You will need the TI-Navigator activity file **8-2 Translating Graphs.act.**

SETTING UP THE ACTIVITY

On the TI-Navigator teacher computer home screen, click the *Activity Center* icon. Choose **File | Load | Load Activity Settings** and load the activity settings file **8-2 Translating Graphs.act.**

Click the **Graph** tab within the Activity Center.

RUNNING THE ACTIVITY

For help logging in, see the Tip Sheet.

1. Prepare students for the activity by explaining that they will explore how to transform the parent absolute-value function, $y = |x|$. Ask them to log in on their calculators and go to the Activity Center.

2. Click **Start Activity.** Students will see two equations on their screen. Y1 contains $y = \text{abs}(x)$, and Y2 is empty.

Q1 Ask, "What will happen to the graph of $y = |x|$ if x is replaced with $x - 3$?" Allow students to suggest possibilities, but don't yet discuss which is correct.

You'll need to have Navigator version 2.1 or higher in order for students to have access to the MATH menu while in NavNet.

3. In Y2, instruct students to enter the new equation, replacing x with $x - 3$. You may need to explain how to enter abs on the calculators. (Press MATH, arrow over to NUM, and press ① (abs).) Ask students to press SEND when finished.

Q2 Again ask, "What happens to the graph of $y = |x|$ if x is replaced with $x - 3$?" [It is translated right three units.]

For help with Quick Polls, see the Tip Sheet.

Q3 Explain that the vertex of an absolute-value graph is the point where the function changes from decreasing to increasing or from increasing to decreasing. Conduct a Quick Poll set to "Open Response" and ask, "What are the coordinates of the vertex of $y = |x|$?" [(0, 0)]

Q4 Conduct a Quick Poll set to "Open Response" and ask, "What are the coordinates of the vertex of $y = |x - 3|$?" [(3, 0)] Ask, "How do these coordinates compare to those of the parent absolute-value function?" [3 is added to the x-coordinate, so it is translated right three units.]

Q5 Ask, "What equation translates $y = |x|$ right four units? Enter your equation in Y2 to check your results." Click **Pause Activity** and discuss the graphs, pointing out any common errors. Click **Resume Activity** and allow students to correct their equations. Conduct a Quick Poll set to "Open Response" and ask, "What are the coordinates of the vertex of this graph?" [$y = |x - 4|$; (4, 0)]

Q6 Ask, "What equation translates $y = |x|$ left five units? Enter your equation in Y2 to check your results." Click **Pause Activity** and discuss the graphs, pointing out any common errors. Click **Resume Activity** and allow students to correct their equations. Conduct a Quick Poll set to "Open Response" and ask, "What are the coordinates of the vertex of this graph?" [$y = |x + 5|$; (−5, 0)]

Q7 Conduct a Quick Poll set to "Open Response" and ask, "What did you replace x with in order to translate the parent absolute-value graph left five units?" [$x + 5$]

4. Click **Stop Activity.** Select all student equations in the Activity Center and delete them. Cover your projection device for a moment and edit the teacher equation to $y = |x + 6|$ and click **Add.** Delete the equation in the Y= box, and select **View | Mask Teacher Input.** This will hide the equation from students. Project the screen again, and click **Start Activity.**

Q8 Ask students to enter into Y2 an equation that will graph the new green graph shown in the Activity Center. Remind them to press MATH to get the absolute-value function.

5. Repeat Step 4 and Q8, changing the graphed equation to $y = |x + 7|$. If you have time, repeat with $y = |x - 3|$.

6. Click **Stop Activity** and delete all student equations. Discuss what students have learned about horizontal translations. Have them write a few sentences summarizing their observations in their notes.

Q9 Explain that now you'll explore what happens when changes are made to y. Ask, "What will happen to the graph of $y = |x|$ if y is replaced with $y + 4$?" Click **Start Activity.** Ask students to enter this new equation into Y2 on their calculators and press SEND. (They'll need to solve for y first.)

For Questions Q10–Q13, you can conduct a class discussion, ask Quick Poll questions, and/or have students submit equations into the Activity Center.

Q10 Again ask, "What happens to the graph of $y = |x|$ if y is replaced with $y + 4$?" [It is translated down four units.]

Q11 Ask, "What are the coordinates of the vertex of this new graph, and how do they compare to the coordinates of the vertex of $y = |x|$?" [$(0, -4)$; 4 is subtracted from the y-coordinate.]

Q12 Ask, "Find an equation that translates $y = |x|$ up five units. What is the vertex?" [$y = |x| + 5$; $(0, 5)$]

7. Click **Stop Activity** and delete all student equations. Cover your projection device for a moment, edit the teacher equation to $y = |x| + 3$, and click **Add.** Delete the equation in the Y= box, select **View | Mask Teacher Input,** project the screen again, and click **Start Activity.**

Q13 Ask students to enter into Y2 an equation that will graph the new green graph shown in the Activity Center.

8. Repeat Step 7 and Q13, changing the graphed equation to $y = |x| - 5$. If you have time, repeat with other equations, such as $y = |x| + 2$ and $y = |x| - 7$. Consider conducting Quick Polls to have students submit the vertices.

9. Repeat Step 7 and Q13, changing the graphed equation to $y = |x - 3| + 2$. If you have time, repeat with other equations, such as $y = |x - 4| - 3$ and $y = |x + 6| - 2$. Consider conducting Quick Polls to have students submit the vertices.

10. Discuss what students have learned about horizontal and vertical translations. Have students write a few sentences summarizing their observations in their notes.

Activity 8.3

In this activity, students follow steps similar to those in Steps 6–10 of the Flipping Graphs investigation. Students use TI-Navigator to explore how to reflect a graph.

Activity Time: 30–40 minutes

PREREQUISITES AND MATERIALS

You will need the TI-Navigator activity file **8-3 Reflecting Graphs.act.**

SETTING UP THE ACTIVITY

On the TI-Navigator teacher computer home screen, click the *Activity Center* icon. Choose **File | Load | Load Activity Settings** and load the activity settings file **8-3 Reflecting Graphs.act.**

Click the **Graph-Equation** tab within the Activity Center.

In the Y= box on the right side of the screen, enter $y = 2^x$ (just type "2^x"), and click **Add.**

RUNNING THE ACTIVITY

For help with logging in and Screen Captures, see the Tip Sheets.

1. On the TI-Navigator teacher computer home screen, click **Begin Class.** Ask students to log in on their calculators, then select 4: EXIT APP. Tell students to work through Steps 1–5 of the Flipping Graphs investigation. Take Screen Captures to monitor progress if you like.

2. Ask students to re-enter NavNet and go to the Activity Center. Explain that they'll explore how the graph of a function changes when x or y is replaced by its opposite.

3. In the Activity Center, click **Start Activity.** Students will receive two empty equations. Ask students to enter $y = 2^x$ into Y1, then press SEND. (You may need to tell students they should enter 2^x using the ^ key on their calculators.) Into Y2, ask students to enter the same equation, but with x replaced by $-x$, then press SEND.

   Q1 Ask, "What change do you notice in the graph?" [It is reflected across the y-axis.]

4. Tell students to now replace y with $-y$ in the equation $y = 2^x$, and enter the new equation into Y2 and press SEND. (Students will need to solve for y, so they'll enter $y = -2^x$.)

   Q2 Ask, "What change do you notice in the graph?" [It is reflected across the x-axis.]

Q3 Ask students to summarize what they've noticed so far. [Replacing x with $-x$ reflects a graph across the y-axis, and replacing y with $-y$ reflects a graph across the x-axis.] Ask, "Do you think the same pattern will hold for any equation?" Click **Pause Activity** and clear all student equations by highlighting them and pressing the Delete key on your computer keyboard. Into the teacher equation, enter $y = 3^x$ and click **Add.**

5. Click **Resume Activity.** Repeat Steps 3, Q1, 4, and Q2 using the function $y = 3^x$. Click **Pause Activity** and clear all student equations.

6. Click **Resume Activity.** Again repeat Steps 3, Q1, 4, and Q2, this time using the function $y = (x - 3)^2$. Click **Pause Activity** and clear all student equations.

7. Click **Resume Activity.** Again repeat Steps 3, Q1, 4, and Q2, this time using the function $y = |x|$. Discuss what happened when x was replaced with $-x$. [There was no change to the graph. This is because the graph is symmetric about the y-axis, so a reflection across the y-axis does not change the graph.]

Q4 Ask students whether the conjecture they made in Q3 seems to hold in all cases.

In this activity, students practice identifying transformations to parent functions, and writing equations to match graphs. This activity can be used in place of Lesson 8.5, or prior to the Lesson 8.5 Activity, Roll, Walk, or Sum.

Activity Time: 40–50 minutes

PREREQUISITES AND MATERIALS

You will need the TI-Navigator activity file **8-5 Transformations.act.**

SETTING UP THE ACTIVITY

On the TI-Navigator teacher computer home screen, click the *Activity Center* icon. Choose **File | Load | Load Activity Settings** and load the activity settings file **8-5 Transformations.act.**

Click the **Graph-Equation** tab within the Activity Center.

RUNNING THE ACTIVITY

1. Explain to students that they'll be identifying transformations to the parent functions $y = x$, $y = |x|$, and $y = x^2$.

2. Begin by reviewing the parent functions students have worked with so far: $y = x$, $y = |x|$, and $y = x^2$. To do this, first enter $y = x$ (just type "x") in the equation box on the right side of the Activity Center screen and click **Add.** Discuss the properties of the resulting graph and have students sketch the line on paper. Then highlight the equation, delete it, and enter the equation $y = |x|$ (type "abs(x)") and click **Add.** Again, discuss and have students sketch the graph. Repeat for $y = x^2$ (type "x^2"). Before you continue, make sure all equations have been deleted.

For help logging in, see the Tip Sheet.

3. On the TI-Navigator home screen, click the **Begin Class** button. Ask students to log in on their calculators and go to the Activity Center. On the teacher computer, go to the Activity Center and click **Start Activity.** Students will receive two blank equations.

4. Write these equations on the board:

   A. $y = x$

   B. $y = x^2$

   C. $y = \text{abs}(x)$

Q1 Ask, "What equation translates the parent absolute-value equation left four units and up two units?" Instruct students to enter their answers into Y1 and press SEND ($\boxed{\text{Y=}}$). [$y = \text{abs}(x + 4) + 2$]

5. Click **Pause Activity,** discuss results, then delete all student responses. To do this, highlight all equations on the right side of the screen and press the **Delete** key on your computer keyboard.

Q2 Ask, "What equation translates the parent quadratic equation right five units?" Instruct students to enter their answers into Y1 and press SEND. [$y = (x - 5)^2$]

6. Click **Pause Activity,** discuss results, then delete all student responses.

7. Hide the projected teacher screen, enter the equation $y = -(x + 2)^2 + 3$, and click **Add.** Delete the equation in the Y= box. Choose **View | Mask Teacher Input.** Then click the **Graph-Equations** tab. Reshow the teacher screen.

For help with Quick Polls, see the Tip Sheet.

8. Do a Quick Poll set to "Multiple Choice A Thru C" and ask, "Which of the functions written on the board is the parent function?" [B] Click **Start Poll** and move the Quick Poll window off the screen so that students cannot see each others' answers. When students are done responding, click **Stop Poll** and discuss answers. Close the Quick Poll window.

Q3 Click **Resume Activity.** Tell students to enter the parent equation ($y = x^2$) into Y1 on their calculators and press SEND.

Q4 Do Quick Polls set to "Yes No" and ask the following three questions. After each Quick Poll, discuss the transformation made to the parent function.

- To get the green graph, has the parent function been translated? [Yes.]

- To get the green graph, has the parent function been reflected? [Yes.]

- To get the green graph, has the parent function been stretched or shrunk? [No.]

Q5 Tell students to enter their guess for the equation of the green graph into Y2 on their calculators. They can press PLOT to view the graph of the equation, and SEND to send it to the teacher computer. The Activity Center is set to allow students to re-enter their equations. Ask students to write a sentence describing how the parent function was transformed to get the green graph.

9. Click **Pause Activity,** return to the **Graph-Equation** tab, and delete all equations from the right side of the screen.

10. Repeat Steps 7–9 (including Q3–Q5) with the equation $y = |x + 2| - 3$. (You'll need to ask students to clear their equations from Y1 and Y2.)

11. Repeat Steps 7–9 (including Q3–Q5) with the equations $y = -(x + 4)^2 - 6$, $y = -2|x - 3| + 8$, and $y = -3(x - 4)$.

Q6 Ask students to write a summary of what they have learned.

These TI-Navigator activities are designed to be used as practice in graphing parabolas in the vertex form $y = a(x - h)^2 \pm k$ or factored form $y = a(x - h)(x - k)$. Students see pictures and graph parabolas to match the picture. You can use the three activity files on the same day or different days.

Activity Time: 10–15 minutes per warm-up

PREREQUISITES AND MATERIALS

You will need the TI-Navigator activity files **9 Basketball Parabola.act, 9 Fountain Parabola.act,** and **9 Fountain2 Parabola.act.**

Students must be familiar with the vertex form or factored form of a quadratic equation.

SETTING UP THE ACTIVITY

On the TI-Navigator teacher computer home screen, click the *Activity Center* icon. Choose **File | Load | Load Activity Settings** and load one of the three files listed above. For the basketball graph, students try to write the equation of a parabola that matches the path of the ball. For the fountain graphs, students can find many different equations for the various parabolic images.

Click the **Graph** tab within the Activity Center.

RUNNING THE WARMUPS

For help logging in, see the Tip Sheet.

1. On the TI-Navigator home screen, click the **Begin Class** button. Ask students to log in on their calculators and go to the Activity Center. Click **Start Activity.** Students will see an image on the projected teacher computer, and will receive one blank equation in their calculators.

2. Instruct students to send an equation that models the path of the ball (for the basketball picture) or matches one of the parabolas (for the fountain picture), then press SEND ([Y=]). For the basketball picture, students' lines are graphed in white, which does not show up against the white background. To remedy this, click the **Graph-Equation** tab, select students' equations, click the square to the right of students' names, select a color, and click **OK.**

3. Click the **Graph-Equation** tab. You may also wish to select **View | Show Student Names.** Then, when you position your mouse over an equation, you will see the

equation and the Display Name of the student to whom it belongs. Also you will see the students' names in the column on the right and the students will want you to select their name to see their equation in blue on the screen. Continue to scroll through the students' names as they make adjustments to their equations. Let students experiment with modifying their equations.

4. When students are satisfied with their equations, click **Pause Activity.**

Q1 Discuss how the values of *a, h,* and *k* affect the graph, and talk about what values students chose and why the value of *a* must be negative.

Q2 Discuss any unusual results and note how many students sent a correct equation.

5. Repeat with another of the three files if desired.

In this activity, students follow steps similar to those in the Rocket Science investigation. TI-Navigator allows students to contribute points to interactively graph the equation, and Quick Polls are used to explore the real-world meaning of features of the graph.

Activity Time: 30–40 minutes

PREREQUISITES AND MATERIALS

You will need the TI-Navigator activity files **9-1 Rocket Science.act** and **9-1 Rollerblader.act.**

SETTING UP THE ACTIVITY

On the TI-Navigator teacher computer home screen, click the *Activity Center* icon. Choose **File | Load | Load Activity Settings** and load the activity settings file **9-1 Rocket Science.act.**

Click the **Graph** tab within the Activity Center.

RUNNING THE ACTIVITY

Part I: In the first part of this activity, students work through the Rocket Science investigation in the student textbook, using TI-Navigator to collaboratively graph the equation, and sharing answers using Quick Poll and Screen Captures.

1. Work through Example A in the student textbook with students. Then introduce the Rocket Science investigation by reading the description of the quadratic motion and giving the equation to students. Give each pair of students a t-value in the range $0 \leq t \leq 12$ to substitute into the equation $h(t) = 0.5(-9.8)t^2 + 50t + 25$. Be sure that students are not in NavNet yet because they will need to calculate their h-value on the home screen. Have them calculate and record the h-value that corresponds to their t-value.

For help logging in, see the Tip Sheet.

2. On the TI-Navigator home screen, click **Begin Class.** Have students log in to NavNet and go to the Activity Center. On the Activity Center home screen, click **Start Activity.** Direct students to line up on the horizontal t-axis (time) on the values that they were given. Next direct students to move straight up to the h-value (height) that they computed earlier, so that they are on the coordinate (t, h), then press MARK. The activity is configured to move in steps of 0.5, so tell students to move to the closest value they can.

3. Click the **Graph-Equation** tab, enter the equation $h(t) = 0.5(-9.8)t^2 + 50t + 25$ in the Y= box (using x in place of t), click **Add,** and see if the curve passes through students' points. Click **Stop Activity.**

4. With the class, discuss Steps 1–3 of the investigation, using the Activity Center graph to point out and discuss answers.

5. Now students will continue working on Steps 5–8 of the Investigation. They can either exit NavNet and enter the $h(t)$ equation manually into the Y= screen, or you can send the equation to students. If you wish to send the equation, go to **Contribute** and select "Equations" from the pull-down menu. Click **Configure,** and the "Configure Calculators for Activity" window will appear. In the **Main Settings** section, choose 1 for "Number of equations per student," and uncheck all three options: "Let students view graphs of equations," "Let students resubmit equations," and "Send current graph contents as background." In the **Students Start with** section, select "Equations below" and enter the equation given in Step 3 above. Click **OK.** Click **Start Activity** and the equation will be sent to students. Click **Stop Activity.** Instruct students to press 2ND [QUIT] and then select 4: EXIT APP.

For help with Screen Captures and Quick Polls, see the Tip Sheet.

6. As students work on Steps 5–8 of the investigation, use Screen Captures or Quick Polls to evaluate their answers. If you do Quick Polls, students will have to re-enter NavNet. Set Quick Polls to "Open Response" and ask questions like those that follow. If you do Screen Captures, tell students to display the appropriate graph or table on their calculator screens, then take a Screen Capture, project it for student viewing, and discuss.

Q1 Click **Start Poll.** Ask, "How high does the rocket fly before falling back to Earth?" [Approximately 152.55 meters.] Click **Stop Poll** and discuss.

Q2 Click **Start Poll.** Ask, "When does the rocket reach its highest point?" [Approximately 5.10 seconds.] Click **Stop Poll** and discuss.

Q3 Click **Start Poll.** Ask, "How long is the rocket in flight?" [Approximately 10.68 seconds.] Click **Stop Poll** and discuss.

7. For Step 9, have students look at a calculator table to approximate the answer. You can show the table in the Activity Center as well by clicking the **Equation** tab, and choosing the appropriate equation using the pull-down menu at the top of the second table column.

8. For Step 10, add the graph of the equation $h = 60$ ($y = 60$) into the Activity Center, point out the point of intersection, and discuss.

9. Select **Edit | Clear Activity Data** to clear all points and equations.

Part II: In the second part of this activity, students see a picture and answer questions about it.

1. In the Activity Center, choose **File | Load | Load Activity Settings** and load the activity settings file **9-1 Rollerblader.act.** Click the **Graph** tab. Students will see an image of a rollerblader's jump. Have students try to visualize the parabola that goes through the knees of the rollerblader.

2. If students are out of NavNet, have them log back in and enter the Activity Center. Students will have control of a point in the coordinate plane. Click **Start Activity.**

3. Direct students to move to the maximum height (of the knees) and press MARK. Click **Pause Activity.** Have students record the coordinates of their point.

4. Click **Resume Activity** and direct students to move to the place on the graph where the rollerblader's knees will hit the horizontal axis. They will need to press NEW and then move and press MARK. Click **Pause Activity.** Again, have students record these coordinates.

5. Click **Resume Activity.** Direct students to move to the place on the graph where the rollerblader's knees are located after he has moved one horizontal unit and press NEW and MARK. Click **Pause Activity** and have students record these coordinates.

6. Click **Resume Activity.** Direct students to move to the point where the rollerblader's knees are 6 units above the horizontal axis and press NEW and MARK. Click **Stop Activity** and have students record these coordinates.

7. Click the **Graph-Equation** tab, enter the equation $y = -1.5x^2 + 4x + 6$ in the Y= box, and click **Add.** A line will appear that approximates the path of the rollerblader's knees. Discuss whether the curve appears to be a good model.

8. Reconfigure the activity to send this equation to students. To do this, go to **Contribute** and select "Equations" from the pull-down menu. The "Configure Calculators for Activity" window will appear. Under the **Main Settings,** choose 1 for "Number of equations per student." Check all three options for "Let students view graphs of equations," "Let students resubmit equations," and "Send current graph contents as background." Under the **Students Start with** section, select "Equation below" and enter $y = -1.5x^2 + 4x + 6$. Click **OK.** Click **Start Activity.** Students will receive the equation. Click **Stop Activity.**

9. Instruct students to exit NavNet and use the equation sent to their calculators to algebraically, numerically, and graphically investigate the questions posed in Steps 3–6 of Part II of this activity:

- What is the maximum height of the rollerblader's knees?

- At what point do the rollerblader's knees hit the horizontal axis?

- Where are the rollerblader's knees located after moving one horizontal unit?

- At what point are the rollerblader's knees 6 units above the horizontal axis?

Compare these answers to the answers found using the original equation.

In this activity, students follow steps similar to those in the Making the Most of It investigation. TI-Navigator allows students to use their own coordinate point to explore the maximization of area. The activity concludes with several Quick Poll questions that help you evaluate student understanding.

Activity Time: 40 minutes

PREREQUISITES AND MATERIALS

You will need the TI-Navigator activity file **9-2 Making The Most.act.**

SETTING UP THE ACTIVITY

On the TI-Navigator teacher computer home screen, click the *Activity Center* icon. Choose **File | Load | Load Activity Settings** and load the activity settings file **9-2 Making The Most.act.** You'll need to set up the activity file's window to accommodate the number of students in your class. (It is currently set for 22 students.) To do this, click the *Edit Window Settings* icon (which shows a red check mark). The set-up directions are as follows:

a. Set the *x*-axis (domain) to have a maximum value of *number of students in your class* +1. If this value is even, set the minimum value to -2. If this value is odd, set the minimum value to -1.

b. To establish the perimeter value for the investigation (instead of 24 in the textbook), double the number of students in your class and add 2.

c. If your number of students is even, set the *y*-axis (range) to have a maximum value of $\left(\dfrac{number\ of\ students}{2} + 1\right)^2$. If your number of students is odd, set the maximum to $\left(\dfrac{number\ of\ students + 1}{2}\right)^2$. Set the minimum value to -1 if the maximum is odd and -2 if the maximum is even.

d. Set the X Scale to 1 and the Y Scale to 4.

Click the **Graph** tab within the Activity Center.

RUNNING THE ACTIVITY

1. Instruct students to do Steps 1 and 2 of the investigation, using the perimeter value you determined in b above.

2. For Steps 3 and 4 of the investigation, click the **Begin Class** button on the TI-Navigator home screen. Ask students to log in on their calculators and go to

For help logging in, see the Tip Sheet.

the Activity Center. Click the *Activity Center* icon, and click the **Start Activity** button. Students will see a graph of width versus area.

3. Select **View | Individualize Student Cursors.** This will replace the generic cursors with icons that are unique for each student. (If there is a check next to this option, it is already selected.) You may also wish to select **View | Show Student Names.** Then, when you position your mouse over a cursor, you will see the coordinates of the cursor and the Display Name of the student to whom it belongs. Be conscious, though, about allowing students the freedom to move anonymously at first.

> In this activity's settings your students have a Step Size of 1. That is, their cursors move 1 unit every time they press an arrow key.

4. Instruct the students to line up on the *x*-axis, making their cursor represent one of the width values. No two students should be on the same point on the *x*-axis. Click **Pause Activity.**

5. Instruct students to move their cursor up to the corresponding area value on the *y*-axis. Click **Resume Activity.** Let the students move around until they have created the parabola. Instruct students to press MARK ([Y=]) to mark their point. Click **Stop Activity.**

Q1 Say, "Describe in detail what the graph looks like." [Downward-facing parabola; The intercepts and maximum will vary, depending on the value your class is using for the perimeter.]

Q2 Ask, "Does it make sense to connect the points with a smooth curve?" [Yes.]

> For help with Quick Polls, see the Tip Sheet.

Q3 Do three Quick Polls set to "Open Response" for the questions in Step 5 of the investigation.

6. Have students exit the Activity Center to work on Step 6. Click the **List-Graph** tab to display for students the coordinates of points on the graph. While students are working, reconfigure the Activity Center to have students contribute equations. To do this, select "Equations" from the **Contribute** pull-down menu, and click **Configure.** Set the number of equations per student to 1, and check "Let students view graphs of equations" and "Send current graph contents as background." Under **Students start with,** select "Empty equations."

7. Return to the **Graph** tab and click **Start Activity.** Instruct students to re-enter NavNet and go to the Activity Center. They'll receive one blank equation. Have them enter their equation from Step 7 and press SEND. Their equations should pass through all the marked points.

8. Revisit the questions in Step 5 of the investigation while looking at the graph.

9. Conduct a class discussion about Step 8, referring back to the graph in the Activity Center.

In this activity, students follow steps similar to those in the Getting to the Root of the Matter investigation. TI-Navigator allows the class to share ideas and "see" each other's work quickly and efficiently.

Activity Time: 40–50 minutes

PREREQUISITES AND MATERIALS

You will need the TI-Navigator activity file **9-4 Factored Form.act.**

SETTING UP THE ACTIVITY

On the TI-Navigator teacher computer home screen, click the *Activity Center* icon. Choose **File | Load | Load Activity Settings** and load the activity settings file **9-4 Factored Form.act.**

Click the **Graph-Equation** tab within the Activity Center.

RUNNING THE ACTIVITY

For help logging in, see the Tip Sheet.

1. In the TI-Navigator home screen, click **Begin Class.** Ask students to log in on their calculators, then exit NavNet.

For help with Screen Captures, see the Tip Sheet.

2. Instruct students to do Steps 1–4 of the Getting to the Root of the Matter investigation. You can take Screen Captures to check student progress.

3. Instruct students to re-enter NavNet and go to the Activity Center. On the Activity Center home screen, click **Start Activity.** Students will receive equations Y1, Y2, and Y3. Y1 contains the equation $y = (x - 4)(x + 3)$. The other two are blank.

Q1 Ask, "What are the roots of the parabola shown in Y1?" [$x = 4$ and $x = -3$]

4. Instruct students to rewrite the equation in standard form, entering the steps into Y2 and Y3. (That is, they'll enter "$y = x^2 + 3x - 4x - 12$" in Y2 and "$y = x^2 - x - 12$" in Y3.) Students can press PLOT after each equation is entered to ensure that the graphs coincide. Instruct them to press SEND when finished. Use Screen Captures to check student progress. Discuss common or interesting mistakes.

5. Click **Stop Activity.** Delete all equations from the right side of the screen. Click **Configure** and change the Y1 equation to $y = (x - 2)(x + 5)$. Click **OK.** Click **Start Activity** and repeat Steps Q1 and 4.

6. Tell students to continue with Steps 5–8 of the Getting to the Root of the Matter investigation.

Activity 9.5

This activity is a follow-up to the Lesson 9.5 Activity, Jump or Roll. TI-Navigator allows students to share their data easily, and see equations that classmates use to try to fit the data gathered. The activity concludes with several Quick Polls that help you evaluate student understanding of quadratic equations in both vertex form and factored form.

Activity Time: 20–30 minutes

PREREQUISITES AND MATERIALS

You will need the TI-Navigator activity files **9-5 Fit Quad Curves 1.act, 9-5 Fit Quad Curves with Pic 1.act, 9-5 Fit Quad Curves 2.act,** and **9-5 Fit Quad Curves with Pic 2.act.**

SETTING UP THE ACTIVITY

From the TI-Navigator teacher computer home screen, click the *Activity Center* icon. Choose **File | Load | Load Activity Settings** and load the activity settings file **9-5 Fit Quad Curves 1.act.**

Click the **Graph** tab within the Activity Center.

RUNNING THE ACTIVITY

1. Tell students that they will be receiving data and finding a curve of best fit for the data.

   For help logging in, see the Tip Sheet.

2. On the TI-Navigator home screen, click **Begin Class.** Ask students to log in and go to the Activity Center. On the teacher computer, go to the Activity Center and click **Start Activity.** Students will receive the four lists L1–L4. Click **Stop Activity.**

   For help with Screen Captures, see the Tip Sheet.

3. Instruct students to exit NavNet. Divide the class into two halves, and have half the class find a curve that fits L1 and L2 and the other half find a curve that fits L3 and L4 (with L1 and L3 representing *x*-coordinates, and L2 and L4 representing *y*-coordinates). (Lists L1–L4 are now stored in students' calculators.) Be sure they enter their equations into Y1. You can take Screen Captures to check student progress if you like.

4. While the class is finding equations to fit the data, reconfigure the activity to receive student equations. To do this, go to **Contribute** and select "Equations" from the pull-down menu. Click the **Configure** button, and the "Configure Calculators for Activity" window will appear. Under the **Main Settings,**

choose 1 for "Number of equations per student," and check options: "Let students view graphs of equations" and "Send current graph contents as background." Under the **Students Start with** section, select "Equations from calculator." Click **OK.** In the Activity Center, click the **Graph-Equation** tab.

5. When students have found an equation and entered it into Y1, ask students to log back in to NavNet and go to the Activity Center. Click **Start Activity.** Students will see the equation that is in Y1 on their calculators. Ask them to press SEND ([Y=]). Students' equations will be graphed on the teacher computer. Click **Stop Activity.** Discuss how well the equations fit the data.

6. Now you'll load the activity settings file that contains an image that matches these points. To do this, choose **File | Load | Load Activity Settings** and load the activity settings file **9-5 Fit Quad Curves with Pic 1.act.** A "Seed data conflict" window will appear. Click **Yes.** Click the *Edit Window Settings* icon and check "Axes." Click **OK.**

For help with Quick Polls, see the Tip Sheet.

Q1 Run Quick Polls set to "Open Response" and ask the questions that follow. Students should primarily answer these questions by looking at the Activity Center graph, perhaps with the help of their equations. You may wish to hide some of the students' parabolas by selecting them on the right side of the screen (hold the Ctrl key to select more than one equation) and clicking **Hide.**

- What is the vertex of the top curve of the hammock parabola? [Approximately $(0, -4.4)$.]

- What are the x-intercepts of the top curve of the hammock parabola? [Approximately 3.4 and -4.]

- What is the factored form of the equation of the top curve of the hammock parabola? [$y = 0.34(x - 3.4)(x + 4)$]

7. You can add the equation in factored form into the teacher equation in the Activity Center to show that it is the same.

In the remainder of this activity, you'll follow steps similar to those above, but with new points and a new image.

8. In the Activity Center, clear all activity data by choosing **Edit | Clear Activity Data** and clicking **Yes.**

9. Choose **File | Load | Load Activity Settings** and load the activity settings file **9-5 Fit Quad Curves 2.act.** On the teacher computer, go to the Activity Center and click **Start Activity.** Students will receive the four lists L1–L4. Click **Stop Activity.**

10. Repeat Steps 3–5 above.

11. Repeat Step 6, loading the activity settings file **9-5 Fit Quad Curves with Pic 2.act.**

Q2 Run Quick Polls set to "Open Response" and ask these questions. Students should primarily answer these questions by looking at the Activity Center graph, perhaps with the help of their equations. You may wish to hide some of the students' parabolas by selecting them on the right side of the screen (hold the Ctrl key to select more than one equation), and clicking **Hide.**

- What is the vertex of the lower parabola? [Approximately $(0, 2.6)$.]

- What are the x-intercepts of the lower parabola? [Approximately -1.9 and 1.7.]

- What is the factored form of the lower parabola? [Approximately $y = -0.8(x + 1.9)(x - 1.7)$.]

This activity uses TI-Navigator as a follow-up to the Slopes investigation. Part I starts with Quick Poll questions to check student understanding of slopes of parallel and perpendicular lines. Then students graph lines that are parallel and perpendicular to a given line. In Part II, vertices of polygons are sent to student calculators, and students find equations of lines through each pair of consecutive vertices and then classify the polygon formed.

Activity Time: Part I: 20 minutes; Part II: 20 minutes

PREREQUISITES AND MATERIALS

For Part I, you will need the TI-Navigator activity file **11-1 Parallel.act.**

For Part II, you will need the list files **11-1_L3.8xl** and **11-1_L4.8xl,** the TI-Navigator activity file **11-1 Quadrilateral.act,** and the image file **11-1 Polygon.jpg.**

SETTING UP THE ACTIVITY

This setup is for Part I of this activity. If you are not doing Part I, skip directly to the Part II section of "Running the Activity."

On the TI-Navigator teacher computer home screen, click the *Activity Center* icon. Choose **File | Load | Load Activity Settings** and load the activity settings file **11-1 Parallel.act.**

Click the **Graph-Equation** tab within the Activity Center. Enter the equation $y = 2x - 3$ in the Y= box on the right side of the screen, and click **Add.**

RUNNING THE ACTIVITY

Part I: In this part of the activity, students answer Quick Poll questions about slopes of parallel and perpendicular lines, then find equations of lines parallel and perpendicular to a given line.

For help logging in, see the Tip Sheet.

1. On the TI-Navigator home screen, click **Begin Class.** Ask students to log in on their calculators and stay at the TI-Navigator home screen.

For help with Quick Polls, see the Tip Sheet.

2. Run Quick Polls set to "Open Response" and ask the following questions:

   • What is the slope of a line parallel to a line with slope 2? [2]

   • What is the slope of a line parallel to a line with equation $y = 3x - 4$? [3]

   • What is the slope of a line perpendicular to a line with slope 2? $\left[-\frac{1}{2}\right]$

   • What is the slope of a line perpendicular to a line with equation $y = -\frac{1}{2}x + 3$? [2]

3. Tell students to enter the Activity Center. On the teacher computer Activity Center home screen, click **Start Activity.** Students will receive two blank equations.

4. Tell students to enter an equation into Y1 that is parallel to the equation graphed on the teacher computer, and enter a perpendicular equation into Y2, then press SEND ([Y=]). Tell students they should not graph the same line as anyone else. Click **Stop Activity.**

Q1 Discuss similarities and differences among student graphs and equations. Highlight a few lines and compare *y*-intercepts. [Parallel lines have equal slope but different *y*-intercepts. Perpendicular lines have opposite reciprocal slopes.]

5. If desired, delete the teacher equation, enter a different equation, click **Start Activity,** and repeat Steps 3, 4, and Q1.

Part II: In the next part of this activity, students identify the quadrilateral with vertices given.

1. Send data lists to student calculators. To do this, in the TI-Navigator teacher computer home screen, click the *Send to Class* icon, select the list files **11-1_L3.8xl** and **11-1_L4.8xl,** and click **Next.** Then select **Class,** check "Force send to students now," and click **Finish.**

2. If students are not already logged in, tell them to log in now. Students will have received L3 and L4 in their calculators. These lists represent the *x*- and *y*-coordinates of the vertices of a quadrilateral.

3. Instruct students to exit NavNet and plot a connected scatter plot of the data that was sent to them. (See **Calculator Note 1H** if students don't remember how to do this.) The plot will be a quadrilateral.

For help with Screen Captures, see the Tip Sheet.

4. Tell students to find an equation through each pair of consecutive vertices. While students are working, you can take Screen Captures to evaluate progress.

5. As students work on finding equations, click the *Activity Center* icon. Choose **File | Load | Load Activity Settings** and load the activity settings file **11-1 Quadrilateral.act.**

6. Instruct students to re-enter NavNet. Click **Start Activity,** and four equations will be pulled from students' calculators when they press SEND.

7. Redisplay the teacher computer Activity Center screen, highlight each equation, and discuss similarities and differences among equations. Note any slopes that are parallel or perpendicular, and also note equations for the same line that are in different forms.

8. Choose **File | Load | Load Background Image** and load the picture **11-1 Polygon.jpg.**

Q1 Ask, "What kind of polygon is this? How do you know?" [Rectangle.]

This activity sequence can either be a follow-up to the In the Middle investigation, or a precursor to Mini-Investigation Exercise 9 on page 604 of *Discovering Algebra.* The activity includes several Quick Poll questions that help you evaluate student understanding.

Activity Time: 40–50 minutes, or 20 minutes if students divide up the work within the group

PREREQUISITES AND MATERIALS

Use this activity only if students are familiar with how to find slope, find midpoints, and write equations given two points.

You will need the list files **11-2_L1.8xl** and **11-2_L2.8xl,** and the TI-Navigator activity file **11-2 Triangle Medians.act.**

SETTING UP THE ACTIVITY

On the TI-Navigator home screen, click the **Begin Class** button. Send the data lists to student calculators. To do this, click the *Send to Class* icon on the TI-Navigator teacher computer home screen, select the list files **11-2_L1.8xl** and **11-2_L2.8xl,** and click **Next.** Then click **Class,** check "Force Send to Student Now," and click **Finish.**

From the TI-Navigator teacher computer home screen, click the *Activity Center* icon. Choose **File | Load | Load Activity Settings** and load the activity settings file **11-2 Triangle Medians.act.**

Click the **Graph** tab within the Activity Center.

RUNNING THE ACTIVITY

For help logging in, see the Tip Sheet.

1. Ask students to log in to NavNet on their calculators. They will receive two lists, which represent the x- and y-coordinates of vertices of a triangle. Tell students to press BACK ($\boxed{\text{ZOOM}}$) after they receive the message "TRANSFERS COMPLETE."

For help with Quick Polls, see the Tip Sheet.

2. Conduct Quick Polls set to "Open Response" and ask the following questions to evaluate whether students understand the midpoint formula:

   • What is the midpoint of the segment connecting $(2, 5)$ and $(3, 1)$? $[(2.5, 3)]$

   • What is the midpoint of the segment connecting $(-2, -3)$ and $(-4, 6)$? $[(-3, 1.5)]$

3. Tell students to exit NavNet (select 4: EXIT APP), plot a connected scatter plot of L1 and L2, and find the equation of the three medians of the triangle formed. (They'll need to find the midpoint of each side of the triangle, then find the slope of the segment connecting each vertex to the midpoint of the opposite side, then write the equation for each median.) If students are in groups, each student or pair of students could work on one of the medians and share with the rest of the group. Instruct students to enter their three equations into Y1, Y2, and Y3 on their calculators. When they are finished, they should log into NavNet again and go to the Activity Center.

4. Click **Start Activity.** Students will see their median equations and should press SEND (Y=).

Q1 Ask, "What do you notice about the medians?" [They intersect at a single point. (This point is called the centroid.)]

In this activity, students use what they have learned in Lessons 11.1 through 11.6. TI-Navigator allows students to receive data that gives the vertices of three quadrilaterals. Then you'll assess students' understanding using a LearningCheck document. This activity can be performed after students have learned the distance formula. The LearningCheck file can be done the following day if necessary.

Activity Time: 40–50 minutes

PREREQUISITES AND MATERIALS

You will need the TI-Navigator activity file **11-6 Quadrilaterals.edc,** the list files **11-6_L1.8xl, 11-6_L2.8xl, 11-6_L3.8xl, 11-6_L4.8xl, 11-6_L5.8xl,** and **11-6_L6.8xl,** and the Student Worksheet that follows this activity.

SETTING UP THE ACTIVITY

Before students start this activity, send the LearningCheck file and data lists to student calculators. To do this, click **Begin Class.** Then click the *Send to Class* icon, select the LearningCheck file **11-6 Quadrilaterals.edc** and the list files **11-6_L1.8xl, 11-6_L2.8xl, 11-6_L3.8xl, 11-6_L4.8xl, 11-6_L5.8xl,** and **11-6_L6.8xl** (hold the Ctrl key to select multiple items), and click **Next.** Then select **Class,** check "Force send to students now," and click **Finish.**

RUNNING THE ACTIVITY

In the first part of this activity, students are sent six lists that represent the vertices of three quadrilaterals. Students will find the equations of the lines that pass through each pair of consecutive vertices, as well as some lengths. They'll use this information to classify quadrilaterals and make conjectures about some new properties of quadrilaterals.

For help logging in, see the Tip Sheet.

1. Ask students to log in on their calculators. Students will receive the six lists and one LearningCheck file. Tell students to press BACK ($\boxed{\text{ZOOM}}$) after they see the message "TRANSFERS COMPLETE." Instruct students to exit NavNet.

2. Pass out the Student Worksheet that accompanies this activity. Explain to students that L1 and L2 are the *x*- and *y*-coordinates of Quadrilateral I, L3 and L4 are the *x*- and *y*-coordinates of Quadrilateral II, and L5 and L6 are the *x*- and *y*-coordinates of Quadrilateral III.

For help with Screen
Captures, see the
Tip Sheet.

3. Instruct students to divide the work within each group and complete the student worksheet. You may wish to take Screen Captures as students work.

4. When students have completed the worksheet, have them complete the LearningCheck file **quadrilaterals.** (If needed, this can be done the next day.) To do this, instruct students to re-enter NavNet and select 2: NETWORK APPS and press ENTER to select LearnChk. Students will see an assignment list. Tell them to arrow down to quadrilaterals and press ENTER. Some of the answers in this assessment will come directly from their worksheets.

5. Students should work through the assessment on their calculators. If this is the first LearningCheck assessment they've done, they'll need some time to experiment and figure out how to navigate through the file and select answers. Write these hints on the board, or distribute the Tip Sheet on page viii:

   • Select PIC or TXT to move between the picture and text for a particular question.

   • Select Q or ANS to move between the question and answer for a particular question.

   • Always press ENTER to select your answer. If you move to the answer but do not press ENTER, your answer will not be recorded.

   • For free response questions, you'll default to typing capital letters. To switch to lowercase letters, press ALPHA once. To switch to numbers, press ALPHA again.

   • For pull-down menus, press any key to see the answer choices.

   • Select NEXT to move to the next question.

   • You can always select MENU to see a list of options. You can go back to the previous item or see a list of items and choose which one you want. You can redo problems if you like. (In the MENU screen, answered questions have a small square next to them.)

6. As students work through the assessment, you can take Screen Captures to view students' calculator screens and check that students are on task and making progress.

Now you'll retrieve the class data.

7. To retrieve class data, click the *Class Analysis* icon.

8. Click the *Collect Answer Files From Classroom Devices* icon to retrieve the data from student handhelds. A "Collect Answer Files from Class" dialog box opens. Check "Delete Answer File from Device after Collect" and "Delete Assignment File from Device after Collect." Then click **Start Transfer.** (If some students did not take the quiz, you'll get an "External Request" message. Click **OK** and then click **Stop** on the left side of the screen, where it says "External Request.")

For more information on how to use Class Analysis, see the TI-Navigator Software Tours or the TI-Navigator Reference Guide.

Answer data is collected from the student calculators and displayed in a spreadsheet. Each student's data is stored as a separate file (called a user file) with the file extension ".usf." The Class Analysis program displays all of these individual files as one spreadsheet. The data will not be lost unless the files are deleted. You can print, save, or view the data in a slide show. Free-response questions must be graded by the teacher.

You'll now display results in a slide show and discuss the results with your class.

9. In the Class Analysis window, click the *Class Results Slide Show* icon. The slide show contains each question followed by a bar chart showing the number of students who entered each answer option. The buttons at the top of the screen allow you to stop the slide show, return to the beginning, move back one slide, move forward one slide, or move to the end of the slide show.

10. Move through the slide show with students and discuss any interesting results. Be sure to point out common mistakes and address how to avoid them.

STUDENT WORKSHEET ANSWERS

Quadrilateral I

1.

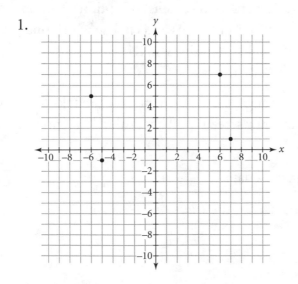

2. a. $y = \frac{1}{6}x - \frac{1}{6}$; b. $y = -6x + 43$; c. $y = \frac{1}{6}x + 6$; d. $y = -6x - 31$

3. a. $\sqrt{148} \approx 12.17$; b. $\sqrt{37} \approx 6.08$; c. $\sqrt{148} \approx 12.17$; d. $\sqrt{37} \approx 6.08$

4. Rectangle. Opposite sides have the same slope and are congruent, and adjacent sides have negative reciprocal slopes. Both diagonals have length $\sqrt{137} \approx 11.70$.

Quadrilateral II

1.

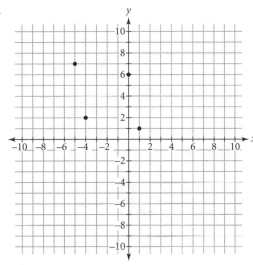

2. a. $y = -\frac{1}{5}x + \frac{6}{5}$; b. $y = -5x + 6$; c. $y = -\frac{1}{5}x + 6$; d. $y = -5x - 18$

3. a. $\sqrt{26} \approx 5.10$; b. $\sqrt{26} \approx 5.10$; c. $\sqrt{26} \approx 5.10$; d. $\sqrt{26} \approx 5.10$

4. Rhombus. Opposite sides have the same slope and all sides are congruent. Both diagonals have length $\sqrt{32} \approx 5.66$.

Quadrilateral III

1.

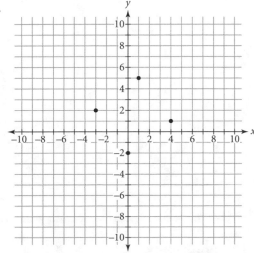

2. a. $y = \frac{3}{4}x + \frac{17}{4}$; b. $y = -\frac{4}{3}x + \frac{19}{3}$; c. $y = \frac{3}{4}x - \frac{33}{4}$; d. $y = -\frac{4}{3}x - 2$

3. a. 5; b. 5; c. 5; d. 5

4. Square. Opposite sides have the same slope and all sides are congruent, and adjacent sides have negative reciprocal slopes. Both diagonals have length $\sqrt{50} \approx 7.07$.

Quadrilateral I

1. Graph the ordered pairs $(-5, -1)$, $(7, 1)$, $(6, 7)$, and $(-6, 5)$ on your calculator and also on this graph:

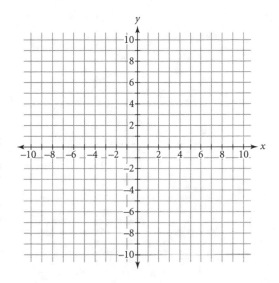

2. Find an equation that passes through each pair of consecutive points:

    a. $(-5, -1)$ and $(7, 1)$

    b. $(7, 1)$ and $(6, 7)$

    c. $(6, 7)$ and $(-6, 5)$

    d. $(6, 5)$ and $(-5, -1)$

3. Find the distance between each pair of consecutive points:

    a. $(-5, -1)$ and $(7, 1)$

    b. $(7, 1)$ and $(6, 7)$

    c. $(6, 7)$ and $(-6, 5)$

    d. $(-6, 5)$ and $(-5, -1)$

4. What kind of polygon has been formed? How do you know? Find the lengths of the diagonals.

Quadrilateral II

1. Graph the ordered pairs $(-4, 2)$, $(1,1)$, $(0, 6)$, and $(-5, 7)$ on your calculator and also on this graph:

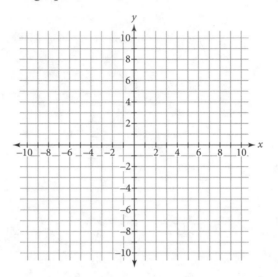

2. Find an equation that passes through each pair of consecutive points:

   a. $(-4, 2)$ and $(1,1)$

   b. $(1, 1)$ and $(0, 6)$

   c. $(0, 6)$ and $(-5, 7)$

   d. $(-5, 7)$ and $(-4, 2)$

3. Find the distance between each pair of consecutive points:

   a. $(-4, 2)$ and $(1, 1)$

   b. $(1, 1)$ and $(0, 6)$

   c. $(0, 6)$ and $(-5, 7)$

   d. $(-5, 7)$ and $(-4, 2)$

4. What kind of polygon has been formed? How do you know? Find the lengths of the diagonals.

Quadrilateral III

1. Graph the ordered pairs $(-3, 2)$, $(1, 5)$, $(4, 1)$, and $(0, -2)$ on your calculator and also on this graph:

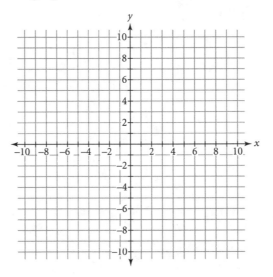

2. Find an equation that passes through each pair of consecutive points:

   a. $(-3, 2)$ and $(1, 5)$

   b. $(1, 5)$ and $(4, 1)$

   c. $(4, 1)$ and $(0, -2)$

   d. $(0,\ \ 2)$ and $(\ \ 3, 2)$

3. Find the distance between each pair of consecutive points:

   a. $(-3, 2)$ and $(1, 5)$

   b. $(1, 5)$ and $(4, 1)$

   c. $(4, 1)$ and $(0, -2)$

   d. $(0, -2)$ and $(-3, 2)$

4. What kind of polygon has been formed? How do you know? Find the lengths of the diagonals.

Comment Form

Please take a moment to provide us with feedback about this book. We are eager to read any comments or suggestions you may have. Once you've filled out this form, simply fold it along the dotted lines and drop it in the mail. We'll pay the postage. Thank you!

Your Name _____

School _____

School Address _____

City/State/Zip _____

Phone _____

Book Title _____

Please list any comments you have about this book.

_____

_____

_____

_____

_____

_____

_____

_____

_____

Do you have any suggestions for improving the student or teacher material?

_____

_____

_____

_____

_____

_____

_____

To request a catalog, or place an order, call us toll free at 800-995-MATH, or send a fax to 800-541-2242.
For more information, visit Key's website at www.keypress.com.

Please detach page, fold on lines and tape edge.